Merry Christ

Wreath
Instructions on p...

*The traditions of Christmas are the structure of holiday joy—like
the decorations we unpack with new delight each holiday season.
Their homey, simple beauty is as heartwarming as a visit from old friends.
Take time to start some family traditions this year.*

Framed Appliqué Picture·Christmas Card

Instructions for Picture on page 18 and for Card on page 11

MERRY
CHRISTMAS

Boxed Ornaments Instructions on page 14

*The handmade gift or decoration is the heart of Christmas—the simple,
loving gesture of rememberance.*
Take a few spare moments to create some of Christmas's wonderful memories.

MERRY CHRISTMAS

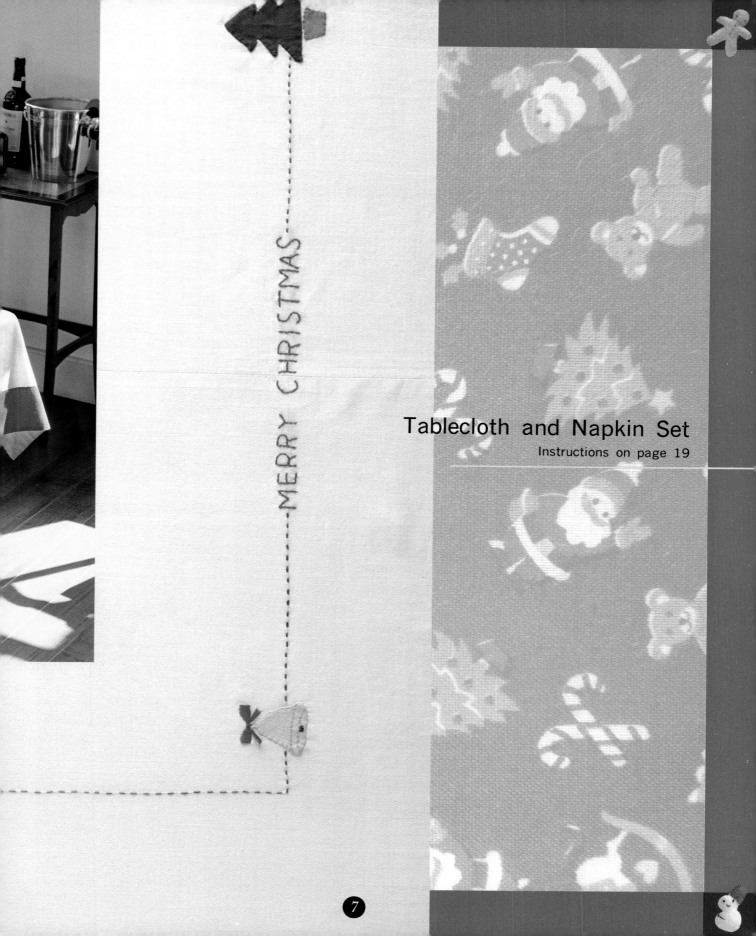

MERRY CHRISTMAS

Tablecloth and Napkin Set

Instructions on page 19

Christmas Ornaments
Instructions on page 16

Cutting Diagrams

Dye sheeting and lace in green.

Body

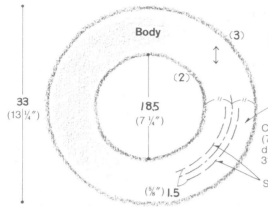

33
($13\frac{1}{4}$")

18.5
($7\frac{1}{4}$")

(2)

(3)

($\frac{5}{8}$") 1.5

Loop   No seam allowance

Sheeting   cut 1   3 ($\frac{1}{4}$")

20 (8")

Add seam allowance indicated in parentheses. Add 1cm ($\frac{3}{8}$") for seam allowance to back piece.

Cut 1 each into doughnut shape 18.5cm ($7\frac{3}{8}$") in inner and 33cm ($13\frac{1}{4}$") in outer diameters, and 19.5cm ($7\frac{3}{4}$") in inner and 31cm ($12\frac{3}{8}$") in outer diameters.

Sew lace edging here.

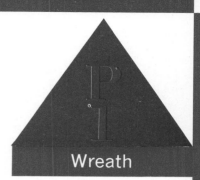

Wreath

Materials: White sheeting, 90cm by 50cm (36"×20"). White cotton lace, 6.5cm by 12m ($2\frac{5}{8}$"× 480"). Checked ribbon: 4cm by 120cm ($1\frac{5}{8}$"×48") and 1.8cm by 90cm ($\frac{3}{4}$"×36"). Felt: Scraps of light brown, white, red, blue, gray, dark brown, pink and apricot pink. 8 large and 22 small beads. Six-strand embroidery floss, No.25 in dark brown and red. Cardboard, 64cm by 33cm ($25\frac{5}{8}$"×$13\frac{1}{4}$"). Polyester fiberfill. Green dye. Glue.
Finished size: 40cm (16") in diameter.

Lace

6.5cm
($2\frac{5}{8}$")

Gathering st.

1cm
($\frac{3}{8}$")

2. Run a gathering stitch in lace edging.
(a) Devide 12m (480") long lace edging into six groups. Run a gathering stitch in each piece changing place of stitching line.
(b) Cut off 1cm ($\frac{3}{8}$") from edge for piece to be placed at top and middle.

Directions

1. Make base in alphabetical order from (a) to (e).
(a) Glue 2 pieces of cardboard together.

(d) Make loop.

(c) Run a gathering stitch along outer edge. Pad with fiberfill and pull thread to fit.

0.8cm

9cm

Turn in seam allowances and overcast.
(e) Slip-stitch back piece to turnings of front catching ends of loop.

Back

Front

Gardboard

Polyester fiberfill

(b) Clip into inner edge of front piece. Pad cardboard with polyester fiberfill, cover with front piece and glue.

3. Sew lace edgings onto base.

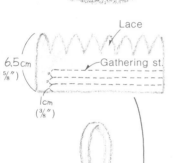

5. Make ornaments and sew in place (see page 10).

6. Sew on beads.

1.8 cm

4 cm

Sew 90cm (36") long ribbon onto center of ruffle.

7. Tie together 50cm (20") long and 70cm (28") long ribbons into bow and sew in place.

1.5cm

(b) For padding, make twisted cord with 6cm ($2\frac{3}{8}$")wide strip and sew in place.

(a) Sew gathered lace together placing second and third pieces lower than first piece.

Patterns for Ornaments (Actual-size)

Cut felt adding no seam allowance except where pieces are overlapped. Overcast two pieces together and stuff with polyester fiberfill. Overcast opening to close. Appliqué ornaments in slip-stitch. Use one strand of dark brown floss unless otherwise indicated.

Santa Claus

Cut one piece from white for back.

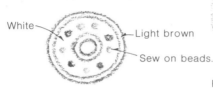

White

Red — Cut one each from felt.

White

Overlap

White

Fly st.

French knot

Apricot pink

Pink — Run a gathering stitch and pull thread. Fill in fiberfill and sew in place.

Doughnut Pie

Don't fill in fiberfill.

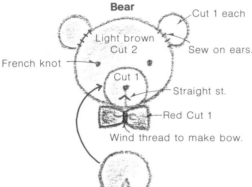

White

Light brown

Sew on beads.

Snow Man

Blue Cut 2

French knot

Fly st.

Straight st.

White Cut 2

Bear

Cut 1 each

Light brown Cut 2

Sew on ears.

French knot

Cut 1

Straight st.

Red Cut 1

Wind thread to make bow.

Sew ends together to fill in fiberfill and sew muzzel in place.

Ginger Boy

French knot

Fly st

Light brown Cut 2

House

Grey Cut 2

Red Cut 2

Red Cut 1

Light brown Cut 2

Back st.

Dark brown Cut

French knot 1 strand of in red

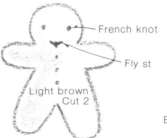
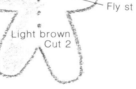
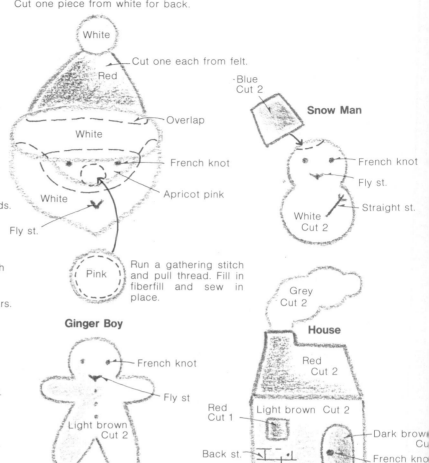
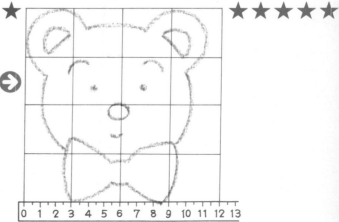

How to enlarge design

Make a larger grid of indicated size and copy design.

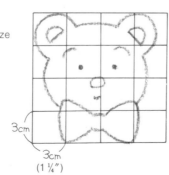

3cm

3cm (1¼")

0 1 2 3 4 5 6 7 8 9 10 11 12 13

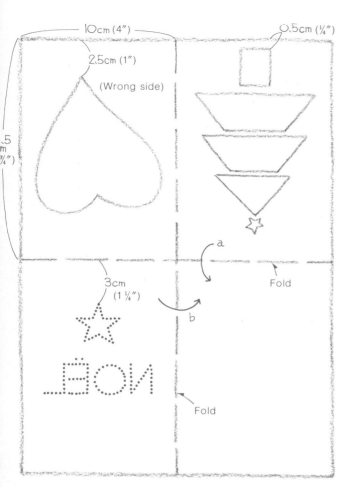

10cm (4")

2.5cm (1")

(Wrong side)

0.5cm (¼")

.5
m
/₄")

3cm
(1 ¼")

a

b

Fold

NOEL

Fold

Directions

1. Cut out heart and tree shapes from cardboard. Perforate star and letters with large needle. Glue fabric onto wrong side.
2. Fold card in half and glue.
3. Fold from fold line.

Materials: Five different prints with X mas designs. Black cardboard, 29cm by 20cm (11 ⅝" × 8"). Scrap of white paper. Glue.
Finished size: See diagrams.

Tree

Glue different fabrics onto wrong side of cut-out shapes.

Actual-size Patterns for Cutting

Cut fabric and backing paper 0.5cm (¹/₄") larger than pattern.

Heart

Apply glue around heart shape and place white paper. Cut out small design from fabric and glue in place.

Print

Letter

Perforate letters and glue fabric on wrong side.

NOEL

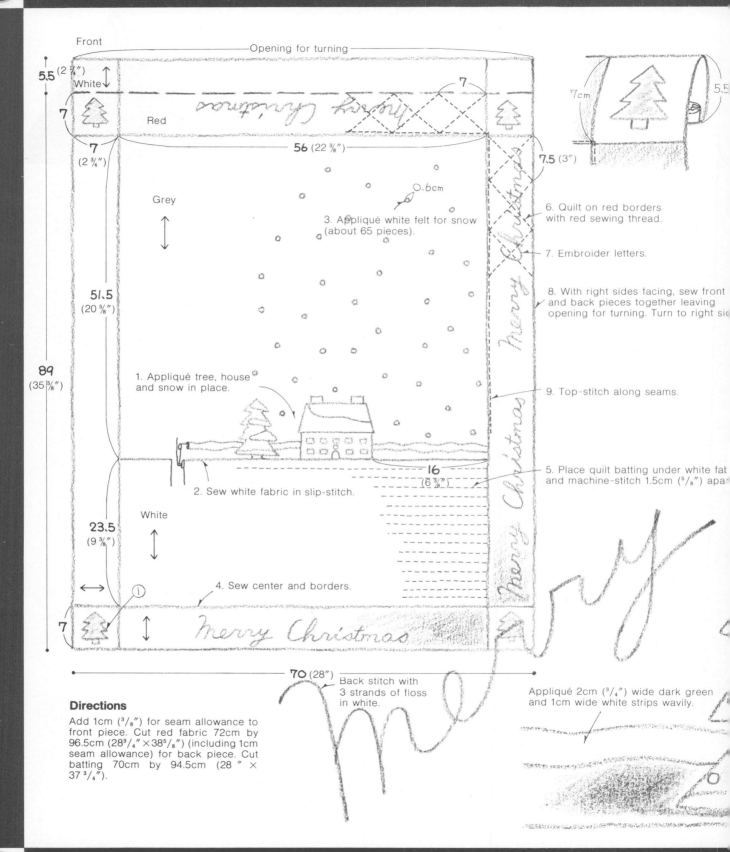

Front

Opening for turning

5.5 (2¼")

White

7

Red

56 (22⅜")

7 (2¾")

7.5 (3")

7cm

5.5

Grey

0.6cm

3. Appliqué white felt for snow (about 65 pieces).

6. Quilt on red borders with red sewing thread.

7. Embroider letters.

8. With right sides facing, sew front and back pieces together leaving opening for turning. Turn to right side.

51.5 (20⅝")

89 (35⅝")

1. Appliqué tree, house and snow in place.

9. Top-stitch along seams.

2. Sew white fabric in slip-stitch.

16 (6⅜")

5. Place quilt batting under white fabric and machine-stitch 1.5cm (⅝") apart.

White

23.5 (9⅜")

4. Sew center and borders.

7

merry Christmas

70 (28")

Back stitch with 3 strands of floss in white.

Appliqué 2cm (¾") wide dark green and 1cm wide white strips wavily.

Directions

Add 1cm (⅜") for seam allowance to front piece. Cut red fabric 72cm by 96.5cm (28¾" × 38⅝") (including 1cm seam allowance) for back piece. Cut batting 70cm by 94.5cm (28" × 37¾").

Wall Hanging

Materials: Cotton fabric: Red, 77cm by 145cm (30 ¾″×58″); gray, 58cm by 54cm (23 ¼″× 21 ⅝″); white 58cm by 45cm (23 ¼″×18″). Cotton fabric for appliqué: Dark green and white, 35cm by 8cm (14″×3 ¼″) each; green, 30cm by 10cm (12″×4″); check and beige, 12cm by 6cm (4 ¾″×2 ⅜″) each; scraps of red, brown and stripes in brown. White felt, 20cm (8″) square. One silver bead, 0.3cm (⅛″) in diameter. 22 pearl beads. Six-strand embroidery floss, No.25 in white, gray, brown, green and red.Quilt batting,70cm by 94.5cm (28″×37 ¾″).
Finished size: 70cm by 89cm (28″×35 ⅝″).

Appliqué and Embroidery Patterns (Actual size)

Add 0.4cm (¹/₈″) for seam allowance to appliqué pieces. Appliqué in slip stitch.

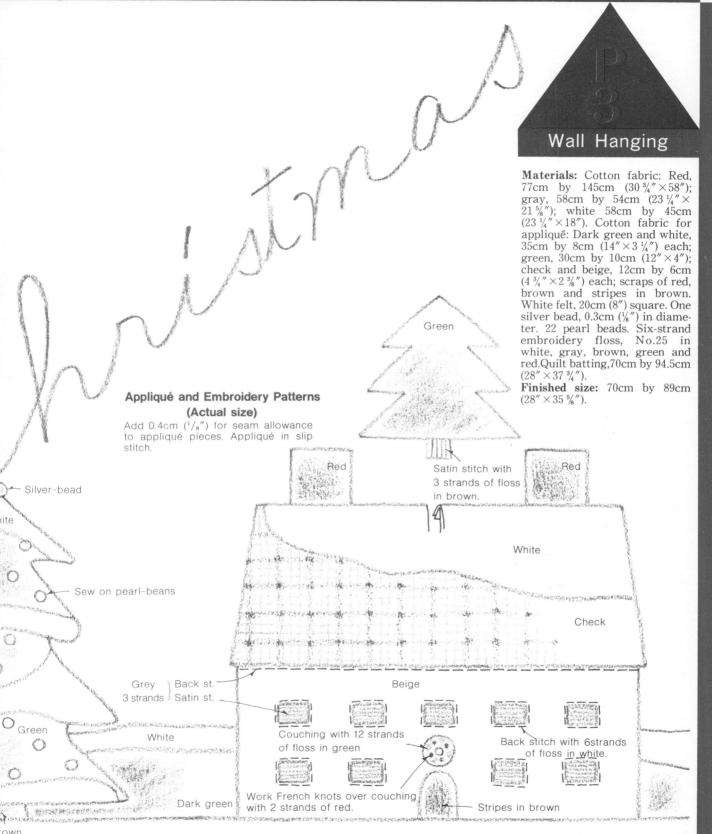

Green

Red

Green

Red

White

Satin stitch with 3 strands of floss in brown.

Silver-bead

White

Sew on pearl-beans

Check

Grey 3 strands } Back st. / Satin st.

Beige

Couching with 12 strands of floss in green

Back stitch with 6strands of floss in white.

Green

White

Work French knots over couching with 2 strands of red.

Stripes in brown

Dark green

rown

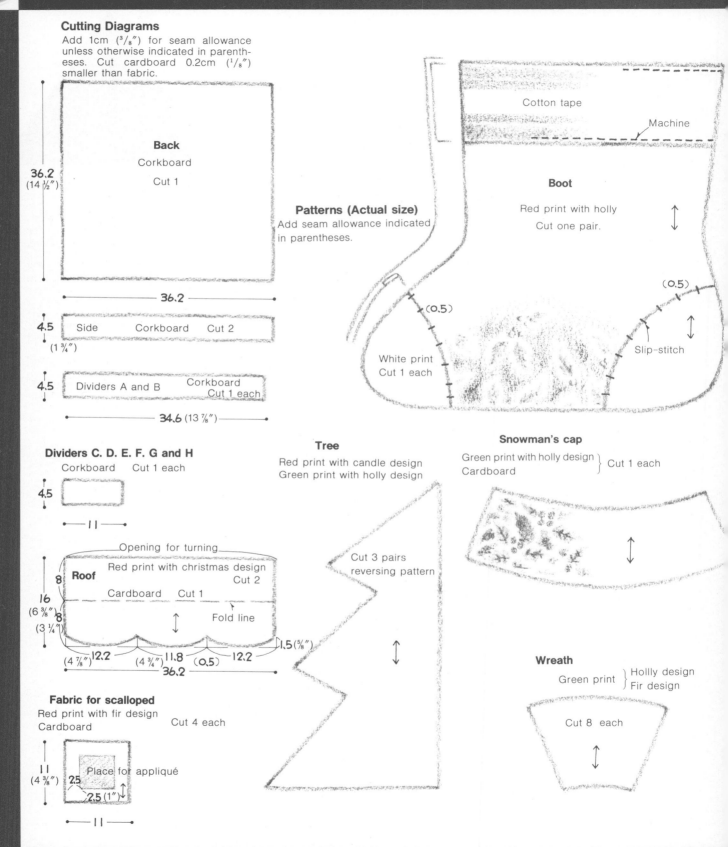

Cutting Diagrams

Add 1cm ($^3/_8$″) for seam allowance unless otherwise indicated in parentheses. Cut cardboard 0.2cm ($^1/_8$″) smaller than fabric.

Back
Corkboard
Cut 1

36.2 (14 $^1/_2$″)

36.2

4.5 (1 $^3/_4$″) Side Corkboard Cut 2

4.5 Dividers A and B Corkboard Cut 1 each

34.6 (13 $^7/_8$″)

Dividers C. D. E. F. G and H
Corkboard Cut 1 each

4.5

11

Opening for turning

8 **Roof** Red print with christmas design Cut 2
16 (6 $^3/_8$″) Cardboard Cut 1
8 (3 $^1/_4$″) Fold line

(4 $^7/_8$″) 12.2 (4 $^3/_4$″) 11.8 (0.5) 12.2 1.5 ($^5/_8$″)
36.2

Fabric for scalloped
Red print with fir design
Cardboard Cut 4 each

11 (4 $^3/_8$″) 2.5 Place for appliqué
2.5 (1″)

11

Patterns (Actual size)
Add seam allowance indicated in parentheses.

Boot
Red print with holly
Cut one pair.

Cotton tape

Machine

(0.5)

(0.5)

Slip-stitch

White print
Cut 1 each

Tree
Red print with candle design
Green print with holly design

Cut 3 pairs
reversing pattern

Snowman's cap
Green print with holly design } Cut 1 each
Cardboard

Wreath
Green print } Hollly design / Fir design

Cut 8 each

Directions

8. Make gift box.

(a) Cover Styrofoam with fabric.

4cm

5cm

5cm

(b) Sew 2 pieces together with right sides facing. Turn to right side.

(c) Place ribbon around box, crossing on top. Pin ends of ribbon at bottom. 20cm(8")long ribbon

in place with pin.

22cm(8¾") long ribbon

(b) Tuck in excess fabric and pin.

9. Embroider and decorate on background fabric (see page 64 for directions).

Pin roof on corkboard.

Fold line

2. Make roof.

(b) Insert cardboard and slip-stitch opening closed.

Fold line

4.5cm

6cm

2cm

(c) Make ribbon into bow tying thread at center and sew in place. Attach bell.

(c) Stuff with polyester fiberfill and slip-stitch opening closed.

1. Assemble box and dividers.

4cm

4cm

4. Make boot.

(a) Appliqué on front.

(d) Sew on pompon.

(a) Sew 2 pieces together with right sides facing.

5. Mark snowman.

C   F

A

MERRY CHRISTMAS

D   G

B

E   H

(a) Glue small and large Styrofoam balls together.

7. Make tree.

(a) Sew 2 kinds of print together with right sides facing. Turn to right side.

0.8cm

Clip into corners

Wrong side

Opening

b) Stuff with polyester fiberfill and slip-stitch.

25cm

2cm

6. Make wreath.

(b) Sew front and back together with right sides facing. Turn to right side and stuff with polyester fiberfill. Slip-stitch opening closed.

Wrong side

Opening

Opening

(a) Sew 8 pieces of print together, alternating 2 kinds of print and leaving end unstitched.

(c) Make hat and pin.

Clip into curve.

Glue fabric onto cardboard.

(d) Push red and black tumbtacks.

(b) Place ribbon around neck and pin. Fray end of ribbon.

(d) Make 25cm (10") ribbon into bow tying thread at center and sew in place. Attach bell.

2cm

(c) Place 7cm (2¾") long ribbon on seams and slip-stitch.

Materiasl: For Box: Red print with Xmas design, 77cm by 18cm (30¾"×7¼"). Satin ribbon, 1cm by 40cm (⅜"×16"). 2 large bells. Cardboard, 37cm by 16cm (14¾"×6⅜"). Corkboard, 0.8cm (⅜") thick, 75cm by 40cm (30"×16"). 10 pins. Glue.

For Boot: Red print with holly design, 22cm by 11cm (8¾"× 4⅜"). Scrap of white print. Cotton tape, 2.3cm by 8cm (⅞"× 3¼"). Pompon. Polyester fiberfill.

For Snowman: Green print with holly design. Cardboard. Satin ribbon, 1cm by 19cm (⅜"×7⅝"). Ball-shaped Styrofoam, 4cm (1⅝") and 5cm (2") in diameter each. 2 black thumbtacks. 0.5cm (¼") in diameter. 1 red thumbtack, 1cm (⅜") in diameter. 2 pins.

For Wreath: Scraps of green prints with holly and fir designs. Ribbon, 0.5cm by 56cm (¼"× 22⅜") and 1cm by 25cm (⅜"× 10"). 1 large bell. Polyester fiberfill.

For Tree: Red print with candle design and green print with holly design, 20cm by 10cm (8"× 4") each. Ribbon, 1cm by 25cm (⅜"×10"). Medium and small bells, one each. Polyester fiberfill.

For Gift Box: Green print with holly design, 25cm by 20cm (10"×8"). Satin ribbon, 1cm by 42cm (⅜"×16¾"). Ribbon with wire, 1.6cm by 35cm (⅝"×14"). Styrofoam, 5cm by 4cm by 5cm (2"×1⅝"×2"). 4 pins.

For Background (for 4 pieces): Red print with fir design, 56cm by 14cm (22⅜"×5⅝") and white cotton fabric, 32cm by 8cm (12¾"×3⅛"). Ribbon, 0.4cm by 16cm (⅛"×6⅜") and 0.6cm by 11cm (¼"×4⅜"). 52 beads. 7 spangles. Six-strand embroidery floss, No.25 in green and red. Cardboard, 22cm (8¾") square. Two-sided adhesive tape.

Finished size: 36.2cm by 40.2cm by 7cm (14½"×16⅛"×2¾").

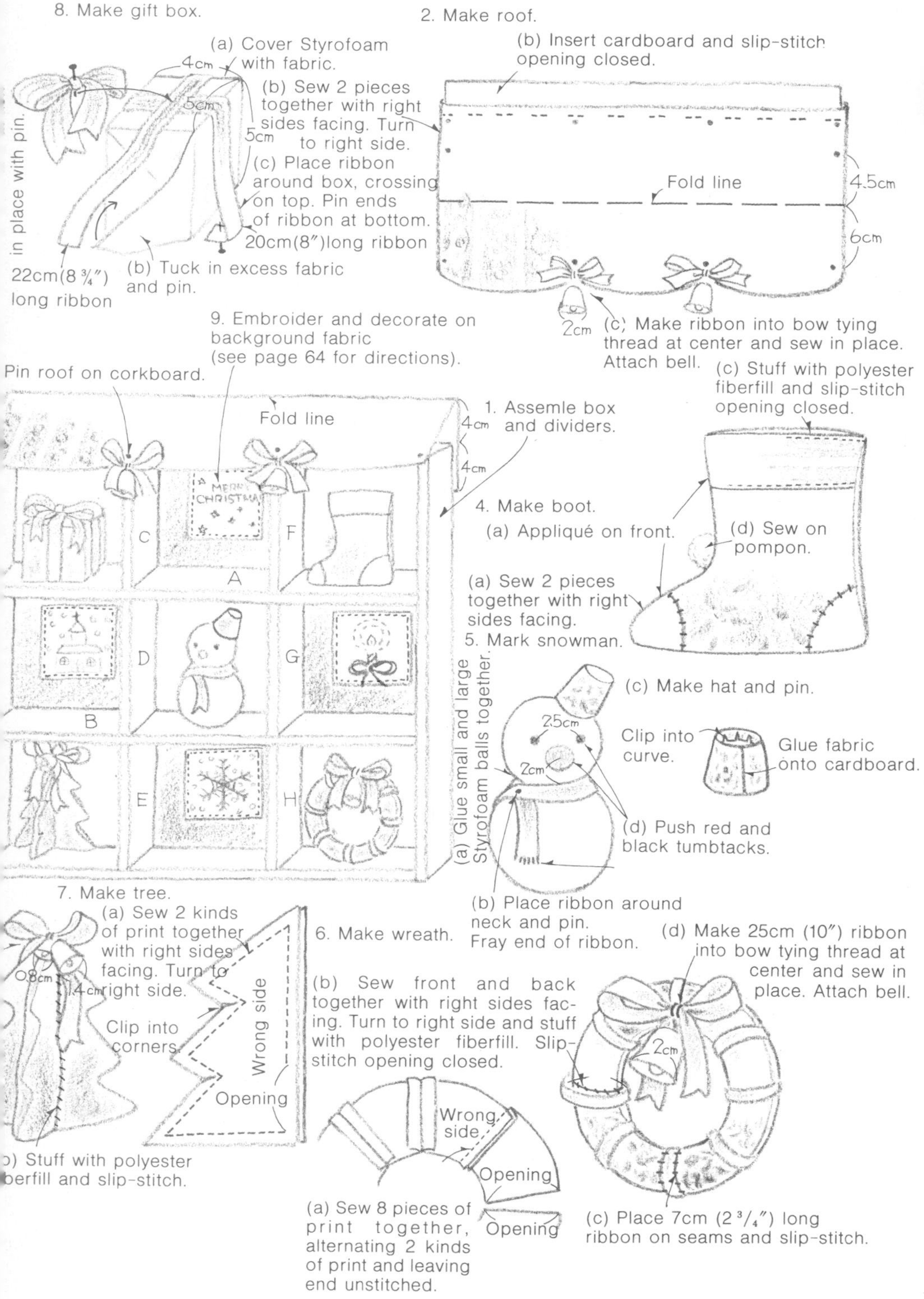

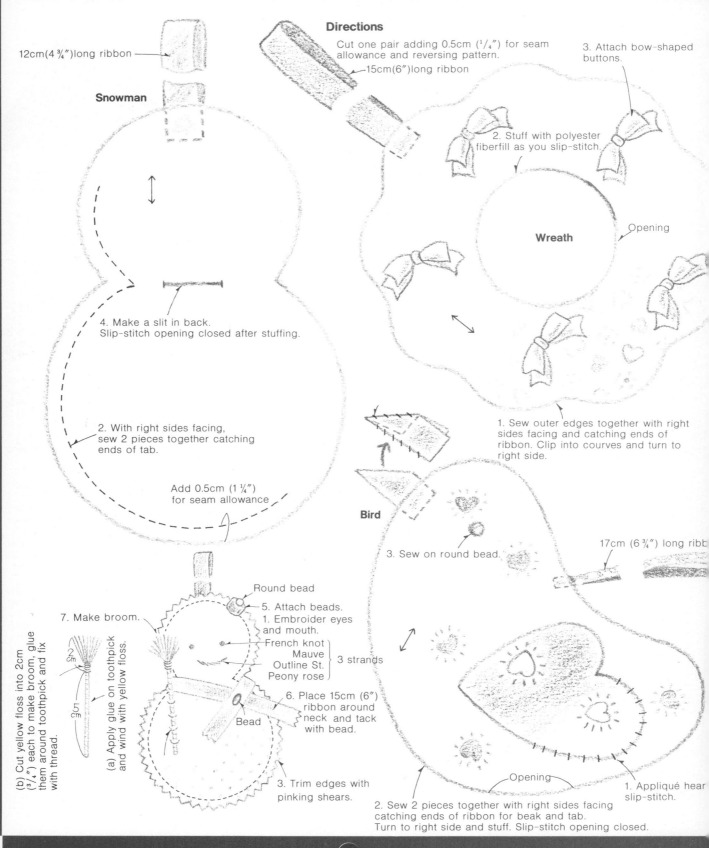

12cm(4 ¾")long ribbon

Snowman

Directions

Cut one pair adding 0.5cm (¼") for seam allowance and reversing pattern.

15cm(6")long ribbon

3. Attach bow-shaped buttons.

2. Stuff with polyester fiberfill as you slip-stitch.

Wreath

Opening

4. Make a slit in back. Slip-stitch opening closed after stuffing.

2. With right sides facing, sew 2 pieces together catching ends of tab.

Add 0.5cm (1 ¼") for seam allowance

1. Sew outer edges together with right sides facing and catching ends of ribbon. Clip into courves and turn to right side.

Bird

3. Sew on round bead.

17cm (6 ¾") long ribb

Round bead

5. Attach beads.

1. Embroider eyes and mouth.

7. Make broom.

French knot
Mauve
Outline St.
Peony rose
} 3 strands

6. Place 15cm (6") ribbon around neck and tack with bead.

Bead

(b) Cut yellow floss into 2cm (¾") each to make broom, glue them around toothpick and fix with thread.

2cm

5cm

(a) Apply glue on toothpick and wind with yellow floss.

3. Trim edges with pinking shears.

1. Appliqué hear slip-stitch.

Opening

2. Sew 2 pieces together with right sides facing catching ends of ribbon for beak and tab. Turn to right side and stuff. Slip-stitch opening closed.

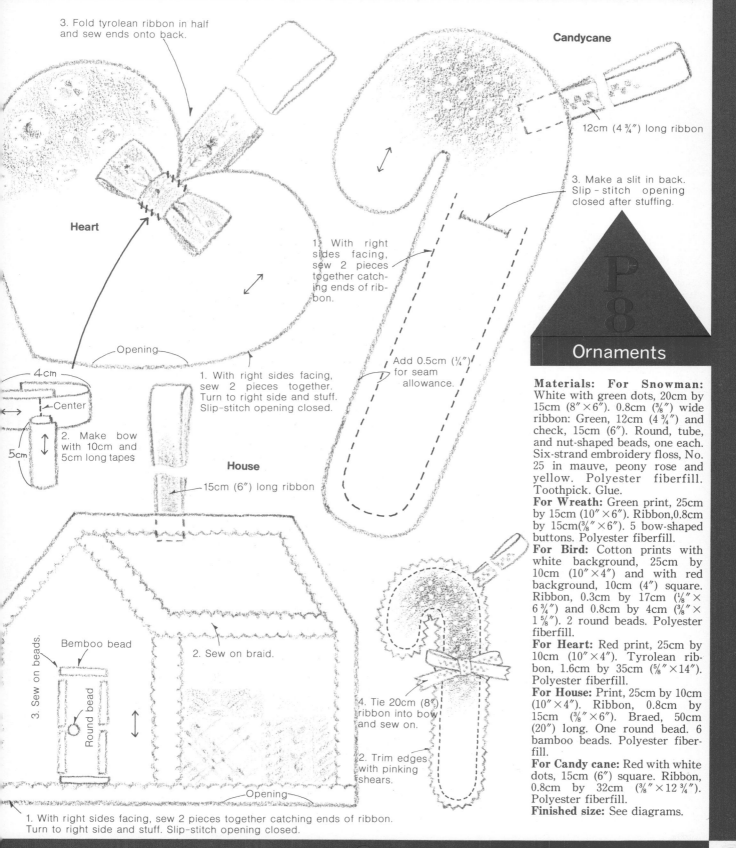

3. Fold tyrolean ribbon in half and sew ends onto back.

Candycane

12cm (4 ¾″) long ribbon

3. Make a slit in back. Slip-stitch opening closed after stuffing.

Heart

1. With right sides facing, sew 2 pieces together catching ends of ribbon.

Add 0.5cm (¼″) for seam allowance.

Opening

— 4cm —

Center

5cm

1. With right sides facing, sew 2 pieces together. Turn to right side and stuff. Slip-stitch opening closed.

2. Make bow with 10cm and 5cm long tapes

House

15cm (6″) long ribbon

3. Sew on beads.

Bemboo bead

Round bead

2. Sew on braid.

4. Tie 20cm (8″) ribbon into bow and sew on.

2. Trim edges with pinking shears.

Opening

1. With right sides facing, sew 2 pieces together catching ends of ribbon. Turn to right side and stuff. Slip-stitch opening closed.

P 8

Ornaments

Materials: For Snowman: White with green dots, 20cm by 15cm (8″×6″). 0.8cm (⅜″) wide ribbon: Green, 12cm (4 ¾″) and check, 15cm (6″). Round, tube, and nut-shaped beads, one each. Six-strand embroidery floss, No. 25 in mauve, peony rose and yellow. Polyester fiberfill. Toothpick. Glue.

For Wreath: Green print, 25cm by 15cm (10″×6″). Ribbon, 0.8cm by 15cm(⅜″×6″). 5 bow-shaped buttons. Polyester fiberfill.

For Bird: Cotton prints with white background, 25cm by 10cm (10″×4″) and with red background, 10cm (4″) square. Ribbon, 0.3cm by 17cm (⅛″× 6 ¾″) and 0.8 by 4cm (⅜″× 1 ⅝″). 2 round beads. Polyester fiberfill.

For Heart: Red print, 25cm by 10cm (10″×4″). Tyrolean ribbon, 1.6cm by 35cm (⅝″×14″). Polyester fiberfill.

For House: Print, 25cm by 10cm (10″×4″). Ribbon, 0.8cm by 15cm (⅜″×6″). Braed, 50cm (20″) long. One round bead. 6 bamboo beads. Polyester fiberfill.

For Candy cane: Red with white dots, 15cm (6″) square. Ribbon, 0.8cm by 32cm (⅜″×12 ¾″). Polyester fiberfill.

Finished size: See diagrams.

Framed Appliqué Picture

Materials: Cotton fabric: Red print with holly design 65cm by 26cm (26″×10⅜″); green, 20cm by 10cm (8″×4″). Unbleached linen, 21cm by 30cm (8⅜″×12″). Various kinds of prints with Xmas design. Felt: Red, 16cm by 11cm (6⅜″×4⅜″); Light brown, 15cm by 10cm (6″×4″). Six-strand embroidery floss, No.25 in dark brown. Gold lamé sewing thread. Nylon sewing thread, 45cm (18″). Pompon with red and lamé thread, 1.5cm (⅝″) in diameter. Frame. Plywood, 20.5 cm by 29.5cm (8¼″×11¾″). 4 wooden nails. Metal hook. Glue. Rouge. Polyester fiberfill.
Finished size: 16.5cm by 25.5cm (6⅝″×10¼″)(inside measurements)

Appliqué designs and patterns (Actual size)

Print

Zigzag-stitch with gold lamé thread.

No seam allowance (Felt and Linen)
Embroider with one strand of dark brown unless otherwise indicated.

Directions

1. Sew triangles at each corner.

2. Appliqué onto background fabric and glue to corkboard.

3. Make bear. Attach bear with nylon thread.

4. Cover each piece for frame with fabric. Trim excess fabric to be over-lapped.

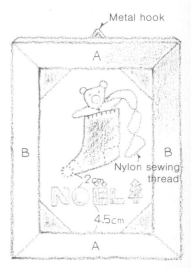

5. Assemble frame and glue fabric to back side.

Cutting Dagrams

Add 1cm (⅜″) for seam allowance
unless otherwise indicated in parentheses

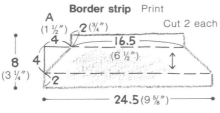

Border strip Print

A Cut 2 each
(1½″) 2 (¾″)
4
16.5
(6½″)
8 (3¼″) 4
2
24.5 (9⅝″)

B
2
4 25.5 (10″)
8
4
2
33.5 (13¼″)

C
3 (1¼″)
23.5 (9¼″)

D
3
28.5 (11¼″)

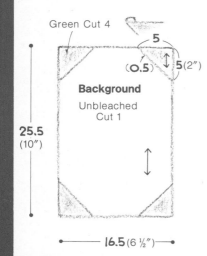

Green Cut 4
5
(0.5) 5 (2″)
Background
Unbleached
Cut 1
25.5 (10″)
16.5 (6½″)

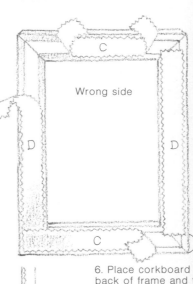

Wrong side
C
D D
C
Plywood

6. Place corkboard back of frame and f with wooden nails a each corner.

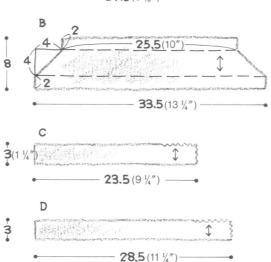

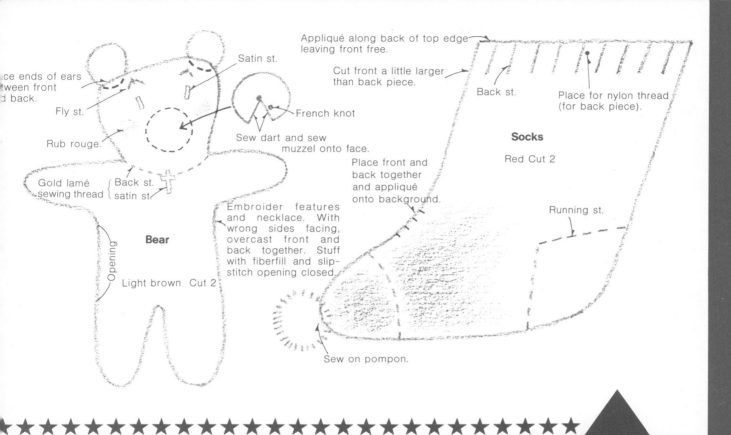

Place ends of ears between front and back.

Fly st.

Rub rouge.

Gold lamé sewing thread { Back st. satin st.

Bear

Light brown Cut 2

Opening

Satin st.

French knot

Sew dart and sew muzzel onto face.

Embroider features and necklace. With wrong sides facing, overcast front and back together. Stuff with fiberfill and slip-stitch opening closed.

Appliqué along back of top edge leaving front free.

Cut front a little larger than back piece.

Back st.

Place for nylon thread (for back piece).

Socks

Red Cut 2

Place front and back together and appliqué onto background.

Running st.

Sew on pompon.

★★★★★★★★★★★★★★★★★★★★★★★★★★★★★★★★★★★★★

Cutting Diagrams · Directions

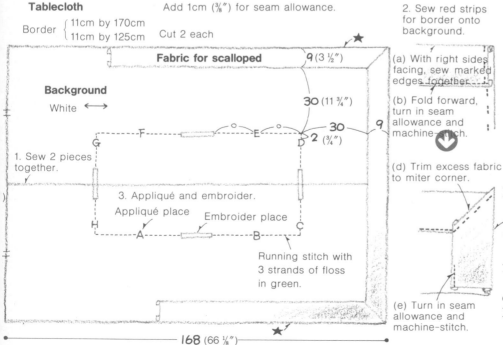

Tablecloth   Add 1cm (³⁄₈″) for seam allowance.

Border { 11cm by 170cm
         11cm by 125cm   Cut 2 each

Fabric for scalloped

Background

White ↔

9 (3½″)

30 (11¾″)

30   9

F   E   D 2 (¾″)

G

1. Sew 2 pieces together.

3. Appliqué and embroider.

Appliqué place   Embroider place

H   A   B   C

Running stitch with 3 strands of floss in green.

168 (66⅛″)

2. Sew red strips for border onto background.

(a) With right sides facing, sew marked edges together.

(b) Fold forward, turn in seam allowance and machine-stitch.

(d) Trim excess fabric to miter corner.

(c) Sew strips onto remaining sides with right sides facing.

(e) Turn in seam allowance and machine-stitch.

P 6

Tablecloth and Napkin Set

Materials: For Tablecloth: Cotton fabric: White, 64cm by 340cm (25⅝″×136″); red, 44cm by 170cm (17⅝″×68″). Scraps of cotton fabric for appliqué. Six-strand embroidery floss, No.25 in red, green, white, gray, light gray, dark brown, orange and cream. Gold lamé thread.
For One Napkin: Several kinds of cotton fabrics for appliqué. Cotton fabric: Red, 33cm (13¼″) square; white, 22cm (8¾″) square. Six-strand embroidery floss, No.25 in same colors as for Tablecloth. Gold lamé thread.
Finished size: Tablecloth, 168cm by 123cm (67¼″×49¼″). Napkin, 28.5cm (11⅜″) square.

Cutting Diagrams · Directions

Napkins

Add seam allowance indicated in parentheses
Make napkins using appliqué patterns A, B, D, E and F.

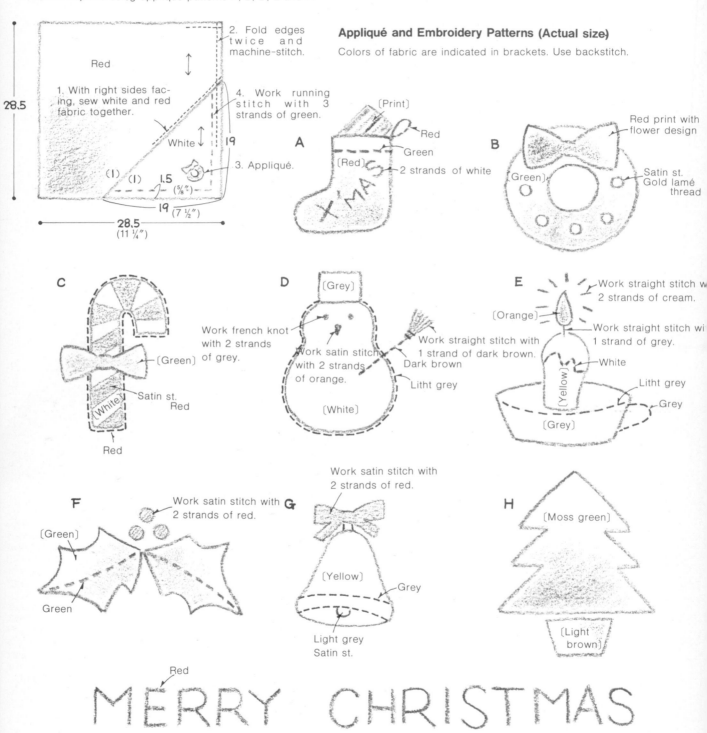

Napkin diagram labels:
- Red
- 28.5
- 1. With right sides facing, sew white and red fabric together.
- White
- 19
- (1) (1) 1.5 (5/8")
- 3. Appliqué.
- 19 (7 1/2")
- 28.5 (11 1/4")
- 2. Fold edges twice and machine-stitch.
- 4. Work running stitch with 3 strands of green.

Appliqué and Embroidery Patterns (Actual size)

Colors of fabric are indicated in brackets. Use backstitch.

A
- [Print]
- Red
- Green
- [Red]
- 2 strands of white
- X'MAS

B
- Red print with flower design
- [Green]
- Satin st. Gold lamé thread

C
- [Green]
- Satin st. Red
- [White]
- Red

D
- [Grey]
- Work french knot with 2 strands of grey.
- Work satin stitch with 2 strands of orange.
- Work straight stitch with 1 strand of dark brown.
- Dark brown
- Litht grey
- [White]

E
- Work straight stitch w 2 strands of cream.
- [Orange]
- Work straight stitch wi 1 strand of grey.
- White
- [Yellow]
- Litht grey
- Grey
- [Grey]

F
- [Green]
- Work satin stitch with 2 strands of red.
- Green

G
- Work satin stitch with 2 strands of red.
- [Yellow]
- Grey
- Light grey Satin st.

H
- [Moss green]
- [Light brown]

Red

MERRY CHRISTMAS

Handmade
Christmas Gifts

Wall Hanging
Instructions on page 30

Don't despair and say you're not creative!
Here are countless new and inventive ways to come bearing gifts
or decorate your own home with delightful country touches.

Gift Box and Bags

Instructions on page 34

Gift Box
Instructions on page 38

Heart-shaped Wall Hanging and Gift Basket

Ihstructions for Wall Hanging on page 44 and for Gift Basket on page 58

Embroidery Patterns

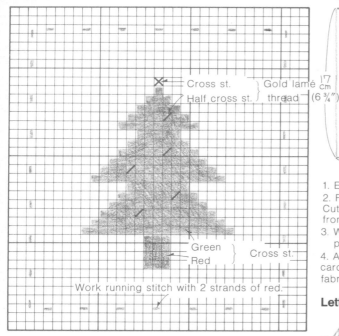

X — Cross st.
— Half cross st. } Gold lamé thread

74 = 37 Meshes

Green
Red } Cross st.

Work running stitch with 2 strands of red.

6.6 = Meshes

Directions

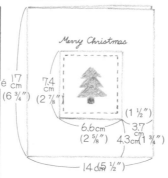

7.4 cm (2 7/8″)
17 cm (6 3/4″)
6.6 cm (2 5/8″)
3.7 cm 4.3 cm (1 3/4″)
(1 1/2″)
14 cm (5 1/2″)

1. Embroider.
2. Fold cardboard in half. Cut out 7.4cm by 6.6cm (3″ × 2 5/8″) from front side to make window.
3. Write greetings with felt-tipped pen.
4. Apply glue in wrong side of cardboard, fit in embroidered fabric and press card to fix.

Letters (Actual size)

Merry Christmas

Christmas Card

Materials: Off-white linen (100 threads per 10cm, 4″), 10cm by 9cm (4″ × 3 5/8″). Six-strand embroidery floss, No.25 in green and red. Gold lamé thread. White cardboard, 28cm by 17cm (11 1/4″ × 6 3/4″). Glue. Black felt-tipped pen.
Finished size: See diagrams.

★ ★

Appliqué Patterns (Actual size)

Add 1cm (3/8″) for margin to background fabric.

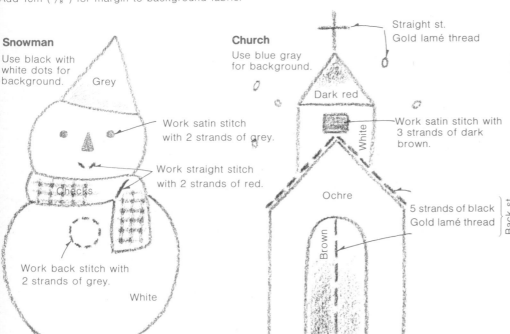

Snowman

Use black with white dots for background.

Grey

Work satin stitch with 2 strands of grey.

Work straight stitch with 2 strands of red.

Checks

Work back stitch with 2 strands of grey.

White

Church

Use blue gray for background.

Straight st. Gold lamé thread

Dark red

White

Work satin stitch with 3 strands of dark brown.

Ochre

Brown

Back st.

5 strands of black Gold lamé thread

Mini Pictures

Materials: For Snowman: Cotton fabric: Black with white dots, 15cm by 10cm (6″ × 4″); scraps of white, gray and checks for appliqué. Six-strand embroidery floss, No.25 in gray and red.
For Church: Blue gray sheeting, 15cm by 10cm (6″ × 4″). Cotton fabric for appliqué in ochre, brown, white and dark red. Six-strand embroidery floss, No.25 in dark brown and black. Gold lamé thread. Oval frame, 11.5cm by 7.5cm (4 5/8″ × 3″) oval (inside measurements).
Finished size: Same size as frame.

P 21

Wall Hanging

Materials: Cotton fabric: Off-white, 90cm (36″) square; green, 90cm by 70cm (36″×28″); 4 different prints, 19cm (7⅝″) square each; check 48cm by 13cm (19¼″×5¼″). Quilt batting, 79cm by 67cm (31⅝″×26¾″). Six-strand embroidery floss, No. 25 in red.

For Gifts: Cotton fabric: White with design, 17cm by 12cm (6¾″×4¾″); red with design, 13cm by 9cm (5¼″×3⅝″). Satin ribbon, 0.6cm by 62cm (¼″×24¾″). String, 10cm (4″). Polyester fiberfill.

For Wreath: Cotton fabric: Green with design, 85cm by 3cm (34″×1¼″); light green, 57cm by 1.5cm (22¾″×⅝″). Satin ribbon, 0.6cm by 22cm (¼″×8¾″). Cardboard, 11.5cm (4⅝″) square. One pinecone.

For Stocking: Cotton fabric: Checks, 30cm by 15cm (12″×6″); scrap of red. Six-strand embroidery floss, No.25 in red. Polyester fiberfill.

For Tree: Cotton fabric: Green with design, 13cm by 15cm (5¼″×6″); scrap of brown.

For Bell: Six-strand embroidery floss, No.25 in green and cherry pink.

For Bear: Cotton fabric: Brown, 15cm by 12cm (6″×4¾″); scrap of dotted print. Satin ribbon, 0.3cm by 18cm (⅛″×7¼″). Six-strand embroidery floss, No.25 in black and dark brown.

For Heart: Red cotton fabric, 13cm by 11cm (5¼″×4⅜″). Scrap of print. Gold lamé thread. Polyester fiberfill.

For Candy cane: Striped cotton fabric, 15cm (6″) square. Satin ribbon, 0.6cm by 17cm (¼″×6¾″).

For House: Red cotton fabric, 13cm by 11cm (5¼″×4⅜″). Green print, 12cm by 6cm (4¾″×2⅜″). Scrap of print with wreath and heart designs.

Finished size: 67cm by 79cm (26¾″×31⅝″).

Cutting Diagrams
Required Amounts of Fabric (including 1cm for seams)

Right side

Piece A ; 19cm (7⅝″) square, off-white print } Cut 4 each

Fabric for patchwork Cut 1
Piece B ; 19 by 6cm (7⅝″×2⅜″), green, Cut 12
Piece C ; 6cm (2⅜″) square, green, Cut 4
Piece D ; 61 by 19cm (24⅜″×7⅝″), green, Cut 1
Piece E ; 48 by 13cm (19¼″×5¼″), check, Cut 1
Piece F ; 38 by 8cm (15¼″×3¼″), off-white, Cut 1

Piece G ; 61 by 7cm (24⅜″×2¾″), green, Cut 4 each
Piece H and I ; 81 by 10cm (32⅜″×4″), green, Cut 1 each

Wrong side
67 by 79cm (26¾″×31⅝″), off-white } Cut1 each
No seam allowance   quilt batting

Directions

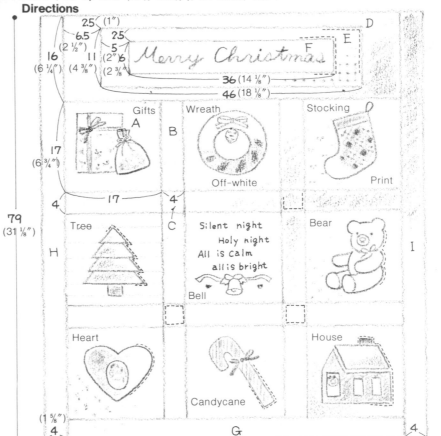

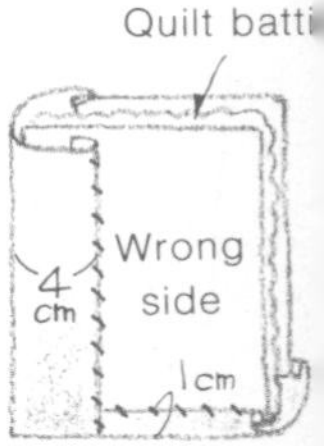

1. Make Gift Box and Bag, Wreath and Stocking.
2. Sew pieces for tree together. Appliqué Tree, Bear, Heart, Candy cane and House in place.
3. Sew piece F onto piece E and embroider letters.
4. Sew piece E onto piece D with running stitch.
5. Sew blocks together with borders and corner squares in between.
6. Pin and baste top, quilt batting and lining together. Quilt along outline of tree, bear, heart, candy cane, house, outside of piece F and inside of piece C.
7. Turn seam allowance of pieces D and G to back and slip-stitch.
8. Sew borders H and I, turn seam allowance to back and slip-stitch.
9. Sew on Gift box and bag, Wreath and Stocking.

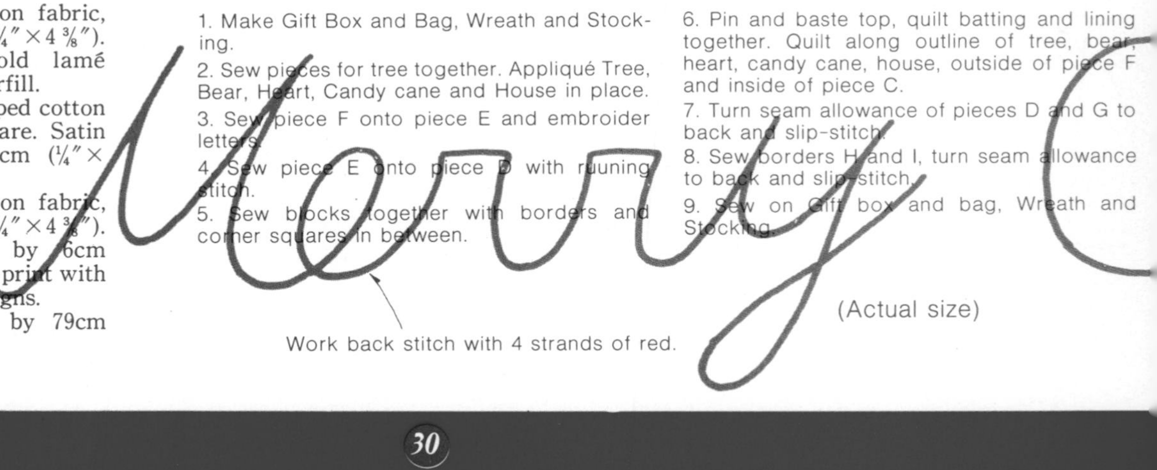

Work back stitch with 4 strands of red.

(Actual size)

Appliqué and Embroidery Patterns

Enlarge patterns to the indicated sizes (see page 10).

Tree

Allow 1cm ($^3/_8$") for folds of patches. Sew pieces of print and off-white together to make strip, then sew strips together to make block.

Center
↓
Off-white

Light green with design (2 $^1/_8$")

5.5
(3")
7.5
(3 $^3/_4$")
9.5
(4 $^1/_2$")
11.5

.5
(
")

.5

3
$^1/_8$")

Brown
2.5
(1")

17 (6 $^3/_4$")

Gift

A

(a) With right sides facing, sew side and bottom seams. Turn to right side and stuff thinly.

(b) Tie box with 23 by 17cm (9 $^1/_4$" × 6 $^3/_4$") ribbon and make knot on back. Slip-stitch one side of ribbon onto front.

(c) Tie 22cm (8 $^3/_4$") long ribbon into bow and sew on. Stuff and tie top edge with cord.

11
(4 $^3/_8$")

White with design
Cut 1

Fold

8
(3 $^1/_8$")

Opening
(No seam allowance)

B

Red with design
Cut 1

8
(3 $^1/_8$")

Fold

6 (2 $^3/_8$")

Wreath

(a) Wind strip A and strip B around cardboard ring (6.5cm (2 $^5/_8$") in inner diameter and 11.5cm (4 $^5/_8$") in outer diameter).

(b) Sew on ribbon bow and attach pinecone. Attach wreath to background at top and bottom without showing any stitches on front.

Strip A (Green with design, 85cm by 3cm)

Strip B (Light green, 57cm by 1.5cm)

Ribbon
Pinecone

11.5
(4 $^1/_2$")

6.5
(2 $^1/_2$")

Bell

Silent night
Holy night
All is calm
all is bright

Back st.
French knot
Green (4 $^1/_2$")

Zig Zag st.
Back st.
Satin st.
Cherry pink

2cm ($^3/_4$")
1.5cm ($^5/_8$")

Candy cane

Strip
Cut 1

Appliqué in slip stitch.

($^1/_4$")
0.5cm

1.5cm

2cm

Tie ribbon into bow and sew on.

Heart

Red Cut 1
1.7cm

Appliqué in slip stitch

Back st.
Gold lamé thread

Stuff fiberfill as you appliqué.

Print Cut 1
Fold
2cm

Stocking

Sew red fabric and check for front. With right sides facing, sew front and back together. Turn to right side and stuff thinly.

0.5cm

Appliqué upper part of stocking.

0.5cm

2cm

Bear

1.5cm

Appliqué in slip stitch.

Sew 4cm (1 $^5/_8$") long ribbon around neck and then sew on ribbon bow.

Satin st.
Back st.
Black

Brown

Back st. Dark brown
Dotted print

Make loop with 6 strands of red.

2cm
0.5 cm

House

Heart designs

Appliqué in slip stitch.

Green print

Red

Wreath design

2cm

Clip at corners, turn seam allowance to back and slip-stitch.

Gift Bags

Materials: For A: Checked fabric, 42cm by 29cm (16 ¾″ × 11 ⅝″). Unbleached cotton fabric, 40cm by 5cm (16″ × 2″). Scraps of red and prints. Ribbon, 0.9cm by 55cm (⅜″ × 22″). Six-strand embroidery floss, No.25 in red.

For B: Unbleached cotton fabric, 32cm by 24cm (12 ¾″ × 9 ⅝″). Scrap of brown fabric for appliqué. Ribbon, 0.8cm by 45cm (⅜″ × 18″). Wooden bead, 1cm (⅜″) in diameter. Six-strand embroidery floss, No.25 in green and white.

Finished size: A, 20cm by 25cm (8″ × 10″). **B,** 15cm by 20cm (6″ × 8″).

Directions

1. Appliqué gingerman on front of A. Sew patched piece with embroidery onto front of B.

2. With right sides facing, sew side bottom seams leaving 5cm (2″) of side open.

3. Top-stitch along side opening first and then along top edges.

4. Insert ribbon into casing and tie ends together. Thread bead onto ribbon before tying for Bag B.

Appliqué and Embroidery Patterns (Actual size)

Add 0.5cm (¼″) for seam allowance.
Make Bag A in alphabetical order from (a) to (c).

Green { Back st. / French knot

Cutting Diagrams

Add seam allowance indicated in parentheses.
Zig-zag-stitch along raw edges.

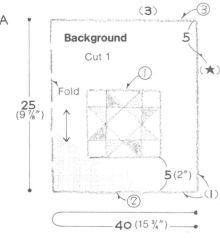

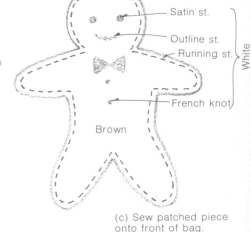

(c) Sew patched piece onto front of bag.

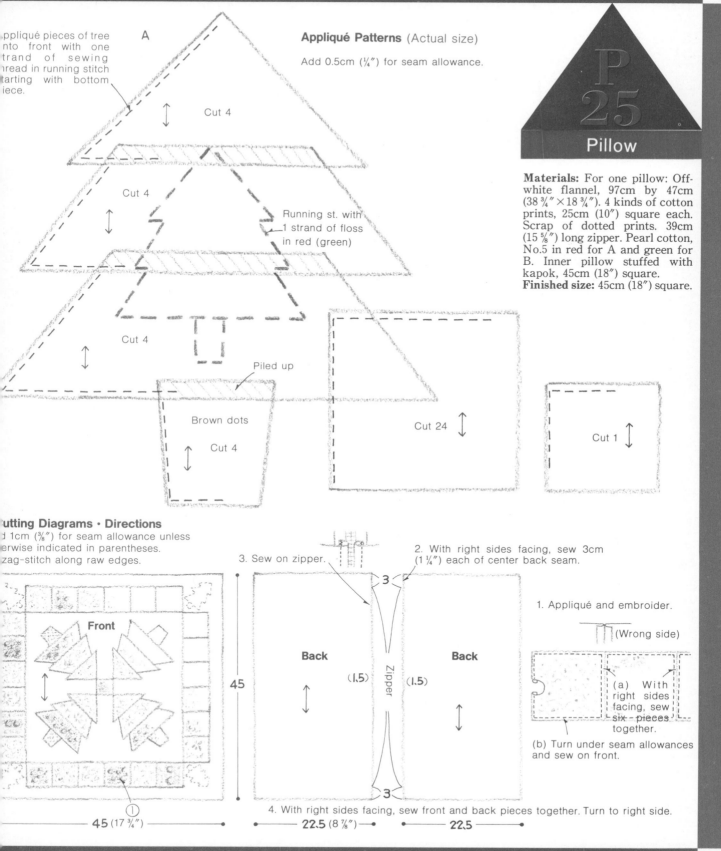

...ppliqué pieces of tree
...nto front with one
...rand of sewing
...read in running stitch
...arting with bottom
...iece.

A

Appliqué Patterns (Actual size)

Add 0.5cm (¼″) for seam allowance.

P 25

Pillow

Cut 4

Cut 4

Running st. with
1 strand of floss
in red (green)

Cut 4

Piled up

Brown dots

Cut 4

Cut 24

Cut 1

Materials: For one pillow: Off-white flannel, 97cm by 47cm (38¾″ × 18¾″). 4 kinds of cotton prints, 25cm (10″) square each. Scrap of dotted prints. 39cm (15⅝″) long zipper. Pearl cotton, No.5 in red for A and green for B. Inner pillow stuffed with kapok, 45cm (18″) square.
Finished size: 45cm (18″) square.

...utting Diagrams · Directions

...d 1cm (⅜″) for seam allowance unless
...erwise indicated in parentheses.
...zag-stitch along raw edges.

3. Sew on zipper.

2. With right sides facing, sew 3cm (1¼″) each of center back seam.

3

Front

Back

(1.5)

Zipper

(1.5)

Back

45

1. Appliqué and embroider.

(Wrong side)

(a) With right sides facing, sew six-pieces together.

(b) Turn under seam allowances and sew on front.

3

4. With right sides facing, sew front and back pieces together. Turn to right side.

①

45 (17¾″)

22.5 (8⅞″)

22.5

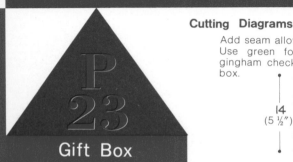

P 23

Gift Box

Materials: Cotton fabric: Green and gingham checks, 54cm by 30cm (21 ⅝″×12″) each; checks, 15cm by 12cm (6″×4 ¾″); off-white, 11cm by 8cm (4 ⅜″×3 ¼″). Ochre grosgrain ribbon, 0.7cm by 17cm(¼″×6 ¾″). One button, 1.5cm (⅝″) in diameter. Six-strand embroidery floss, No. 25 in green. Cardboard, 35cm by 30cm (14″×12″). Quilt batting, 50cm (20″) square. Glue.

Finished size: 17cm by 13cm by 7.5cm (6 ¾″×5 ¼″×3″).

Cutting Diagrams

Add seam allowance indicated in parentheses. Use green for outside and gingham checks for inside of box.

No seam allowance (Cardboard. Quilt batting) Cut batting on fold at marked places.

Lid
Outside
Inside
Cut 1 each
14 (5 ½″)
18 (7 ⅛″)

Lid
Cardboard
Quilt batting
Cut 1 each
13
17 (5 ⅛″)

Side piece A
Bottom Outside Inside Cut 1 each
B
Side piece B
A
7.5 (3″) — 17 (6 ¾″) — 7.5
7.5
13
7.5

Cardboard
Quilt batting
Cut 1 each
12
16 (6 ¼″)

Side piece B
Side piece A
Cardboard
Quilt batting
Cut 2 each
7 (2 ¾″)
7

Appliqué

A Check
B Off-white
Quilt batting
Cut 1 each
11 (4 ⅜″)
1.5
14 (5 ½″)

Directions

Glue batting onto front and back of cardboard.

Batting
Cardboard

Loop Green Cut 1
1.5 (⅝″)
7

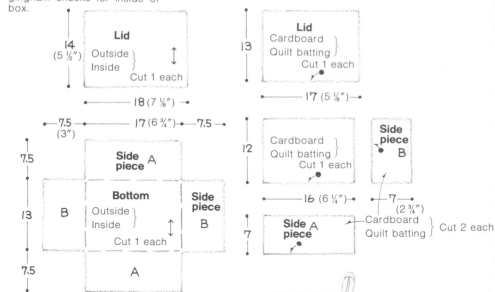

3. Overcast top edge of side piece and lid together.

1.5cm
4. Sew on button.

1. Make lid first.

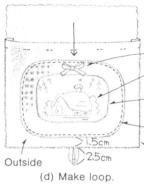
Outside
1.5cm
2.5cm
(d) Make loop.

0.5cm
Turn in seam allowance and slip-stitch.

(g) Insert padded cardboard between front and back. Turn in seam allowance and slip-stitch.

(f) Tie ribbon into bow and sew on.

(a) Place off-white fabric and batting together and embroider.

(b) Turn under seam allowance of checked fabric, place along off-white fabric and slip-stitch.

(c) Sew joined piece onto front of lid in running stitch.

(e) With right sides facing, sew front and back together catching ends of loop in place. Turn to right side.

2. With right sides of side and bottom pieces facing, sew outer and lining fabric together.

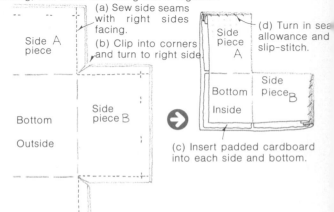

Side A piece
Bottom
Side piece B
Bottom
Outside

(a) Sew side seams with right sides facing.
(b) Clip into corners and turn to right side.

Side Piece A
Bottom Inside
Side Piece B
(d) Turn in seam allowance and slip-stitch.

(c) Insert padded cardboard into each side and bottom.

Cutting Diagrams   Add 1cm (⅜″) for seam allowance

Bottom Side

Cut each piece into 7cm (2 ¾″) -30cm (12″) long, join them together to make 370cm (148″) long strip.

Handle

Cut 50cm (20″) each from red and green prints excluding seam allowance.

Materials: Several kinds of red and green prints. Quilt batting, 120cm by 70cm (48″×28″). **Finished size:** See diagrams.

Directions

1. Sew pieces together and cover rolled batting to make long cord.

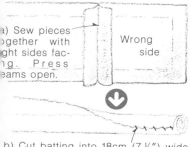

(a) Sew pieces together with right sides facing. Press seams open.

Wrong side

(b) Cut batting into 18cm (7 ¼″) wide strips. Roll up batting lengthwise and slip-stitch along edge.

Quilt batting

1.5cm

(c) Cover rolled batting with joined piece and slip-stitch along edge.

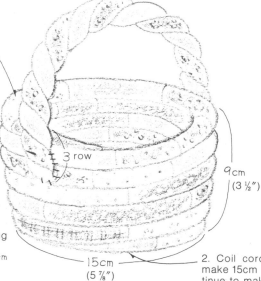

3 row

9cm (3 ½″)

15cm (5 ⅞″)

2. Coil cord and overcast edges to make 15cm (6″) disc for bottom. Continue to make side in same manner.

Handle

1cm

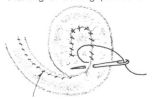

Starting of coiling (inside of bottom).

Coil cord without showing seams.

End of coiling (inside of side)

Slip-stitch end of cord onto inner edge.

★ ★

Embroidery Pattern (Actual side)

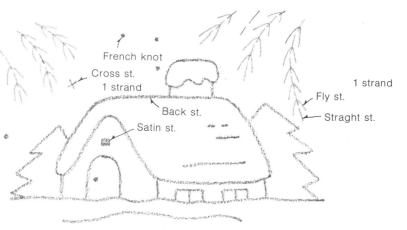

French knot

Cross st. 1 strand

Back st.

Satin st.

1 strand

Fly st.

Straght st.

P 25
Stocking

Materials For one: Unbleached Aida cloth (41 threads per 10cm, 4″), unbleached heavy-weight cotton fabric and iron-on interfacing, 12cm (4¾″) square each. Pearl cotton, No.5 (see list below for colors).
Finished size: 9.5cm (3¾″) in diameter.

Patterns and Directions

Press iron-on interfacing onto wrong side of flannel.

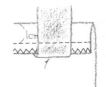

4. Turn in seam allowance of top edge and stitch catching ends of tape for hanging.

5. Work running stitch with red floss.

(1.5)

1cm

2cm

1cm

1. Appliqué print strips with one strand of white sewing thread in running stitch.

Print Cut 1 each

6. Attach broom with yarn and tie yarn into bow.

|24¾″)

28
(11″)

24.5cm(9⅝″)

3. With right sides facing, sew front and back together. Turn to right side.

2. Sew cotton tape in place.

Cotton tape

Print
Cut 1 each

①

Front and Backside

Flannel
Iron-on interfacing } Cut one pair ↕

0.5cm(¼″)

2cm (¾″)

2cm

Cutting Diagrams

dd 1cm (³⁄₈″) for seam allowance.

Aida cloth
Heavy-weight cotton fabric
Iron-on interfacing

Cut 1 each

9.5

Directions

2. With right sides facing, sew front and back together leaving opening for turning. Turn to right side and slip-stitch opening closed.

Opening for turning

3

1. Embroider on front. Press interfacing on wrong side of Aida cloth.

3. Couch 2 strands of moss green along seam with one strand of green sewing thread.

Coasters

Materials: Flannel and iron-on interfacing, 55cm by 35cm (22″ × 14″) each. 5 different prints in red. Cotton tape, 1.7cm by 65cm (⅝″ × 26″). Pearl cotton, No.5 in red. 13cm (5 ¼″) long broom.
Finished size: See diagrams.

Patterns

Present

☆

◿ = Blue

△ = Dark brown

⊙ = Yellow

☒ = Light blue

⬚ = Mahogany brown

▢ = White

▨ = Red

▩ = Green

▨ = Pink

Center

Center

Cake

Center

Center

House

Center

Center

Tree

Center

Center

Glass

Center

Center

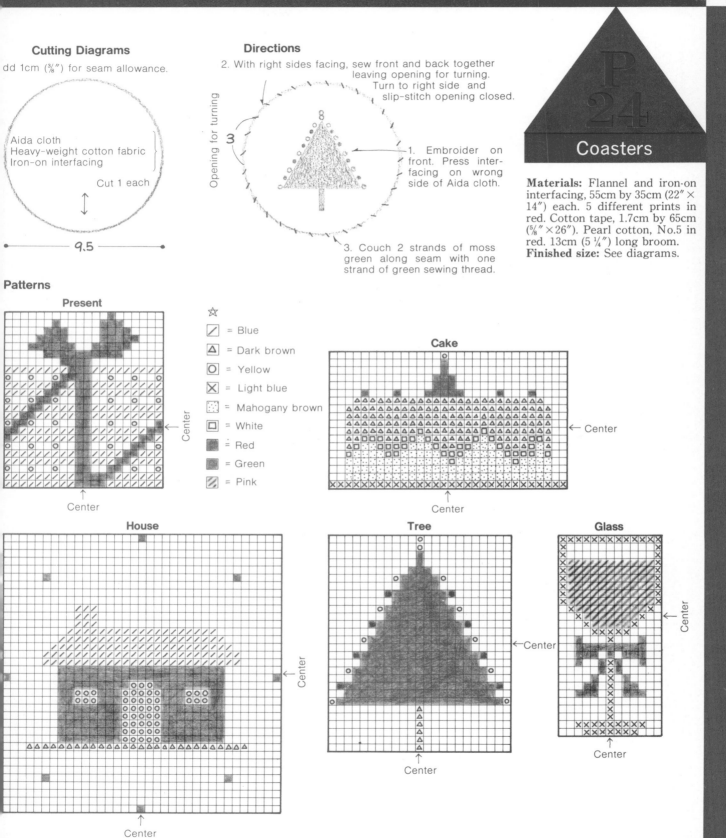

P26

Gift Box

Materials: Cotton prints: Red with fir design and green with Xmas design, 90cm by 25cm (36″×10″) each; white with holly design, 74cm by 26cm (29 ⅝″× 10 ⅜″). Cotton fabric for appliqué: White, 25cm by 15cm (10″× 6″); red with holly design, 10cm (4″) square; green with fir design, 14cm by 5cm (5 ⅝″×2″); scrap of green with X mas design. Satin ribbon: Green, 0.5 cm(¼″) by 1m(40″); red, 1cm by 21cm (⅜″×8 ⅜″) and 0.3cm by 35cm (⅛″×14″). Beads: Gold, 96 pieces; white, 18 pieces. One star-shaped spangle. Gold lamé thread. 2 bells. Iron-on interfacing, 90cm by 75cm(36″×30″). Cardboard, 60cm by 50cm (24″× 20″). Polyester fiberfill. Glue. Two-sided adhesive tape.
Finished size: 20cm by 14cm by 21cm (8″×5 ⅝″×8 ⅜″).

Cutting Diagrams

Add 0.5cm (¼″) for seam allowance unless otherwise indicated in parentheses. Cut cardboard into separate pieces from fold lines (cut one whole piece for chimney).

Side
Red with fir design cotton prints
Green with Xmas design cotton prints } Cut 1 each
Iron-on interfacing······Cut 2
Cardboard······Cut 1 each

Chimney
White with holly design cotton prints
Iron-on interfacing } Cut 2 each
Cardboard········Cut 1

Roof
Cardboard········Cut 1
White with holly design cotton prints
Iron-on interfacing Cut 2 ea

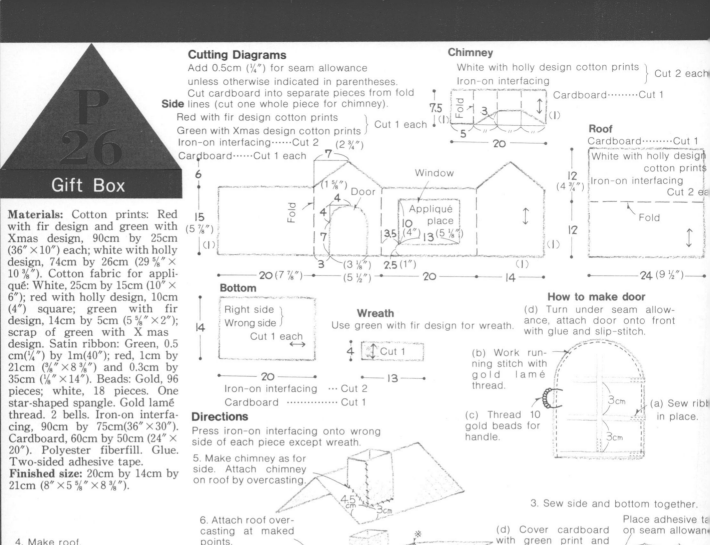

Bottom
Right side
Wrong side } Cut 1 each
Iron-on interfacing ··· Cut 2
Cardboard ·············· Cut 1

Wreath
Use green with fir design for wreath.
4 Cut 1

How to make door
(a) Sew ribbon in place.
(b) Work running stitch with gold lamé thread.
(c) Thread 10 gold beads for handle.
(d) Turn under seam allowance, attach door onto front with glue and slip-stitch.

Directions

Press iron-on interfacing onto wrong side of each piece except wreath.

5. Make chimney as for side. Attach chimney on roof by overcasting.

6. Attach roof overcasting at maked points.

3. Sew side and bottom together.

(d) Cover cardboard with green print and place at bottom.

Place adhesive tape on seam allowance.

(c) Place two-sided adhesive tape on seam allowance.

1. Appliqué door and window in place.

4. Make roof.

(a) With right sides facing, sew two pieces together.
(b) Insert cardboard.
0.2cm
(c) Top-stitch twice along fold line.
(d) Insert another cardboard. Turn in seam allowance and slip-stitch.
Cardboard

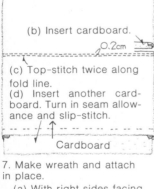

2. Make side following instructions below.
(d) Overcast edges of side.
(b) Clip into corners (marked places) and turn to right side. Machine-stitch along fold line.

(a) With right sides facing, sew red and green prints together leaving bottom edge open.

(a) With right sides facing, sew outer piece of bottom and marked side together.
(b) Turn under seam allowance and overcast three sides.

(c) Insert cardboard between red and green prints.

7. Make wreath and attach in place.
(a) With right sides facing, fold strip in half lengthwise and stitch. Turn to right side and stuff. Join ends by overcasting.
(b) Tie 35cm (14″) long ribbon around wreath.
(c) Shape ribbon into bow by tying thread at center and sew in place.
(d) Attach 2 bells.

Cutting Diagrams and directions

Add 1cm (⅜") for seam allowance
unless otherwise indicated in parentheses. White with design Cut 1

1. Embroider on powder green strip.
2. Appliqué strips on front.
3. Make bow and sew on. With right sides facing, sew [fro]nt and back together. Turn [to] right side. Insert inner pillow [an]d slip-stitch opening closed.

How to make bow

[Ma]ke pieces (a), (b) and (c). [C]enter seam with right [f]acing.

[Tur]n ends of piece (a) to [turni]ng. Tie with piece (b) at

[Ma]ke tuck at center of [pie]ce and sew on.

Bow   Powder green
A Cut 1   Fold
8 (3⅛")
25 (9⅞")

B Cut 1   C Cut 2
8
6 (2⅜")   10 (4")   1.5 (⅝")

Appliqué strips
Powder green
4
15 (5⅞")
13 (5⅛")
28 (11")
4 (1⅝")
28

For Pillow B

Green with design Cut 1
Make Pillow B as for A. Add wreath on ribbon bow.

10 (4")
10
Opening for turning
4
11 (4⅜")
11
White with holly design.
28

Wreath

Green with design   Cut 1
5
15

How to make wreath

(a) With right sides facing, sew edges to gether.
Turn to right side and stuff with fiberfill.
(b) Overcast ends to form ring.
(c) Sew on bow.
(d) Attach bell.

P 49
Pillow

Materials: Cotton fabric:
For A: White with design, 60cm by 30cm (24"×12"); powder green, 45cm by 30cm (18"×12").
For B: Green with design, 60cm by 36cm (24"×14⅜"); white with holly design, 55cm by 30cm (22"×12"). Six-strand embroidery floss, No.25 in red for A. One red bell for B. Inner pillow stuffed with kapok, 30cm (12") square.
Finished size: 28cm (11¼") square.

Patterns (Actual size)

Back st. 3 strands

Merry Christmas

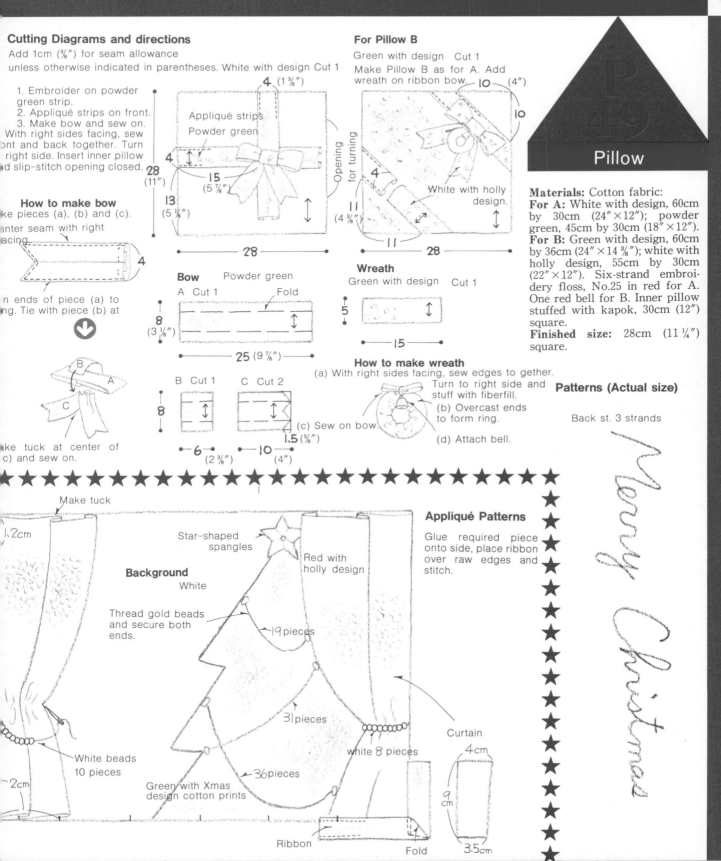

Make tuck
1.2cm
Star-shaped spangles
Red with holly design

Background
White

Thread gold beads and secure both ends.

19 pieces

31 pieces

white 8 pieces

36 pieces

White beads 10 pieces

2cm

Green with Xmas design cotton prints

Ribbon   Fold

Appliqué Patterns

Glue required piece onto side, place ribbon over raw edges and stitch.

Curtain
4cm
9 cm
3.5cm

Materials: Bulky yarn (50g = 80m), 120g (4 ¼ oz) white and 80g (2 ⅞ oz) black for Pillow A; 120g (4 ¼ oz) brown, 80g (2 ⅞ oz) white and small amount of black. Small amount each of silver red and green. One pair of knitting needles, size 9 (5.7mm). Inner pillow stuffed with kapok, 40cm (16″) square.

Finished size: 40cm (16″) square.

Directions: Use one strand of yarn. Work in stockinette stitch following chart. Make back piece as for front. With wrong sides facing, overcast three sides. Insert inner pillow and overcast opening closed.

Colorwork in stockinette stitch
Make Pillow B in same manner changing colors and design of bear.

Satin stitch with 1 strand of floss in black.

Straight stitch with 1 strand of floss in green.

Chain stitch   Bullion knot 2 strands of floss in red.

Outline stitch with 1 strand of floss in white.

Black

White

starting ←

Gauge:
In stockinette stitch
16.5 sts=10cm (4″)
17.5 rows=10cm (4″)

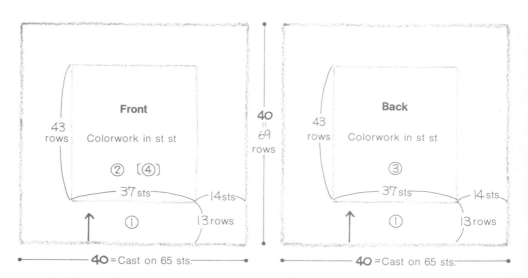

Front
Colorwork in st st
② 〔④〕
43 rows
37 sts   14 sts
13 rows
40 = Cast on 65 sts.

40 = 69 rows

Back
Colorwork in st st
③
43 rows
37 sts   14 sts
13 rows
40 = Cast on 65 sts.

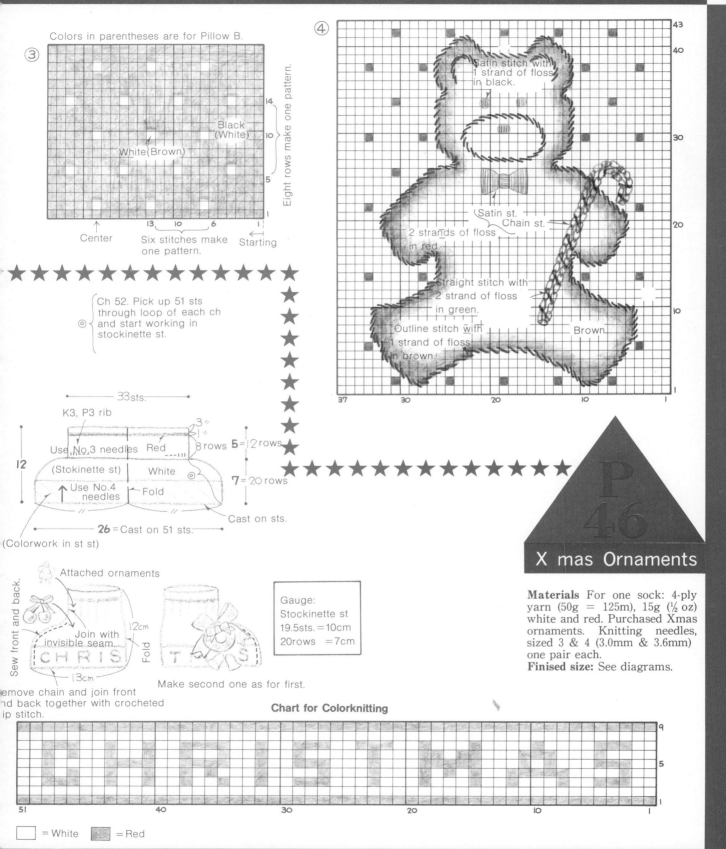

③ Colors in parentheses are for Pillow B.

Eight rows make one pattern.

14
10
Black (White)
White(Brown)
5
1

Center
13 10 6
Six stitches make one pattern.
Starting

④
43
40
Satin stitch with 1 strand of floss in black.
30
Satin st.
Chain st.
20
2 strands of floss in red.
Straight stitch with 2 strand of floss in green.
10
Outline stitch with 1 strand of floss in brown.
Brown.
37 30 20 10 1

★ ★ ★ ★ ★ ★ ★ ★ ★ ★ ★ ★ ★ ★ ★

◎ Ch 52. Pick up 51 sts through loop of each ch and start working in stockinette st.

★
★
★
★
★
★
★
★
★
★

33sts.
K3, P3 rib
3″
1″
Use No.3 needles   Red
8 rows   5 = 12 rows
(Stokinette st)   White
12
Use No.4 needles   Fold   7 = 20 rows
◎
Cast on sts.
26 = Cast on 51 sts.
(Colorwork in st st)

★ ★ ★ ★ ★ ★ ★ ★ ★ ★ ★ ★ ★ ★ ★ ★

Attached ornaments
Sew front and back.
Join with invisible seam.
12cm
Fold
CHRIS
13cm
emove chain and join front nd back together with crocheted ip stitch.

Make second one as for first.

Gauge:
Stockinette st
19.5sts. = 10cm
20rows = 7cm

P 46

X mas Ornaments

Materials For one sock: 4-ply yarn (50g = 125m), 15g (½ oz) white and red. Purchased Xmas ornaments. Knitting needles, sized 3 & 4 (3.0mm & 3.6mm) one pair each.
Finised size: See diagrams.

Chart for Colorknitting

9
5
1
51 40 30 20 10 1

☐ = White   ▨ = Red

Knitted X mas Stockings

Materials: For A: Bulky yarn (50g = 83m): Red and green, 20g (¾ oz) each. For B: White, 50g (1¾ oz) and green, 10g (⅜ oz). Ribbon, 2cm by 80cm (¾″×32″). For C: Bulky yarn (50g = 83cm): Red, 50g (1¾ oz) and small amount of white. Purchased X mas ornaments. For D: Bulky yarn (50g = 83m): Red 50g (1¾ oz) and green, 15g (½ oz). Ribbon, 2cm by 55cm (¾″×22″). 2 bells. Beads and star-shaped spangles. Knitting needles, sizes 5 & 7 (3.9mm & 4.5mm) one pair each.

Finished size: See diagrams.

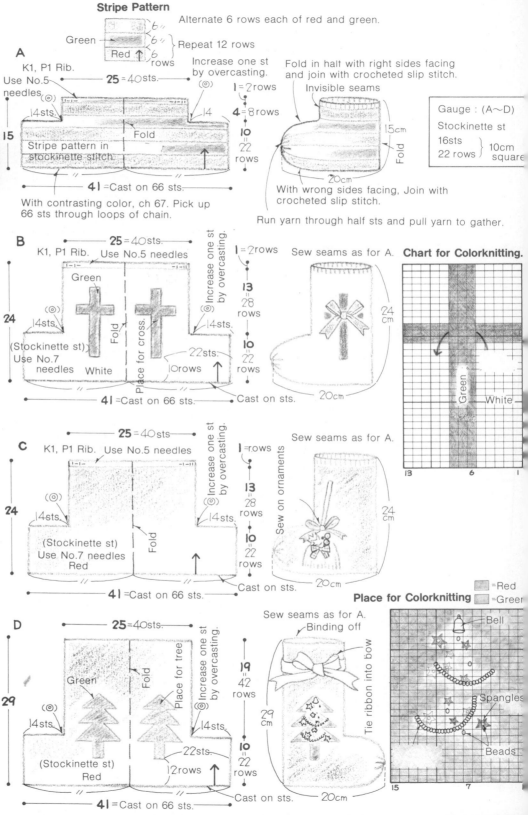

Stripe Pattern

Alternate 6 rows each of red and green.

Green — 6″
Repeat 12 rows
Red ↑ 6 rows

A

K1, P1 Rib. Use No.5 needles

25 = 40 sts.

Increase one st by overcasting.

14 sts.

15

Fold

Stripe pattern in stockinette stitch.

I = 2 rows
4 = 8 rows
10
22 rows
14

41 = Cast on 66 sts.

With contrasting color, ch 67. Pick up 66 sts through loops of chain.

Fold in half with right sides facing and join with crocheted slip stitch.

Invisible seams

15cm

Fold

20cm

With wrong sides facing, Join with crocheted slip stitch.

Run yarn through half sts and pull yarn to gather.

Gauge : (A~D)
Stockinette st
16 sts } 10cm
22 rows } square

B

K1, P1 Rib. Use No.5 needles

25 = 40 sts.

Increase one st by overcasting.

Green

24

14 sts.

Fold

(Stockinette st) Use No.7 needles White

Place for cross.

22 sts.
10 rows

I = 2 rows
13
28 rows
14 sts.
10
22 rows

41 = Cast on 66 sts. Cast on sts.

Sew seams as for A.

24 cm

20 cm

Chart for Colorknitting.

Green   White

13   6   1

C

K1, P1 Rib. Use No.5 needles

25 = 40 sts.

Increase one st by overcasting.

24

14 sts.

(Stockinette st) Use No.7 needles Red

Fold

I = rows
13
28 rows
14 sts.
10
22 rows

41 = Cast on 66 sts. Cast on sts.

Sew seams as for A.

Sew on ornaments

24 cm

20 cm

= Red
= Green

D

25 = 40 sts.

Increase one st by overcasting.

29

14 sts.

Green

Fold

Place for tree

(Stockinette st) Red

22 sts.
12 rows

I = rows
19
42 rows
10
22 rows

14 sts.

41 = Cast on 66 sts. Cast on sts.

Sew seams as for A.
Binding off

Tie ribbon into bow

29 cm

20 cm

Place for Colorknitting

Bell

Spangles

Beads

15   7

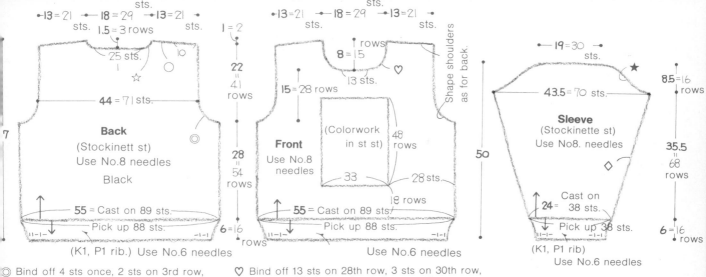

Back
(Stockinett st)
Use No.8 needles
Black

• 13 = 21 sts. • 18 = 29 sts. • 13 = 21 sts.
1.5 = 3 rows
25 sts.
10
☆
44 = 71 sts.

55 = Cast on 89 sts.
Pick up 88 sts.
(K1, P1 rib.) Use No.6 needles

1 = 2
22
41 rows
28
54 rows
6 = 16 rows
7

Front
Use No.8 needles

• 13 = 21 sts. • 18 = 29 sts. • 13 = 21 sts.
rows
8 = 15
13 sts.
♥
Shape shoulders as for back.
15 = 28 rows
(Colorwork in st st)
48 rows
33
28 sts.
18 rows
55 = Cast on 89 sts.
Pick up 88 sts.
Use No.6 needles
50

Sleeve
(Stockinette st)
Use No8. needles

• 19 = 30 sts. •
★
43.5 = 70 sts.
◇
24
Cast on 38 sts.
Pick up 38 sts.
(K1, P1 rib)
Use No.6 needles
8.5 = 16 rows
35.5
68 rows
6 = 16 rows

◎ Bind off 4 sts once, 2 sts on 3rd row, dec 1 st every other row twice and 1 st every 4th row once.

◯ Bind off 10 sts on 41st row from underarm and 11 sts on 43rd row.

☆ Bind off 25 sts on 40th row, and 2 sts on 42nd row.

♥ Bind off 13 sts on 28th row, 3 sts on 30th row, 2 sts on 32nd row, dec 1 st every other row twice, every 4th row once and work even 3 rows.

◇ Increase 1 st every 4th row 16 times and work even 4 rows.

★ Bind off 4 sts on 68th row, 3 sts on 70th row, dec 2 sts every other row twice, 1 st every other row twice, 2 sts every other row twice, 1 st every other row twice, 2 sts every other row once, bind off 5 sts every other row once and work one row.

Chart for Colorknitting

Gold lamé) Bullion Knot
Red   ) 1 strand
Lazy Daisy stitch with 2 strands of fross in green.

☐ = Black   ▨ = Gray   ⊘ = Gold lamé   ▦ = Red

Gauge:
Stockinette st
16 sts }
19 rows } 10cm squanre

Neckband
(K1, P1 rib)
Use No.6 needles
Pick up 31 sts. 3 = 8 rows
Pick up 49 sts.

P 47

Sweater

Materials: Bulky yarn (50g = 83m): Black, 430g (15 ⅜ oz); red and gray, 15g (½ oz) each; small amount each of green and gold lamé yarn. Knitting needles, size 8 (4.8mm) one pair and size 6 (4.2mm) one pair and set of four.
Finished size: Bust, 110cm (44″). Length, 57cm (22 ¾″). Width, 44cm (17 ⅝″). Sleeve length, 50cm (20″).
Directions: Work with one strand of yarn in stockinette stitch following chart. Make wreath design on front. After completing front, embroider leaves and berries. Work in K1, P1 rib along sleeve and bottom edges. Then join shoulder seams and work in K1, P1 rib around neck edge. Sew side and underarm seams. Set in sleeves.

Appliqué designs · Patterns (Actual size) and Directions

Glue appliqué pieces onto background fabric and zigzag-stitch.

3. Appliqué onto cotton fabric.

2. Press interfacing on wrong side of cotton fabric.

1. Cut 2 pieces from cotton fabric adding 1cm (⅜″) for seam allowance.

Iron-on interfacing } No seam
Flannel } allowance
Cardboard } Cut 1 each

4. Run a gathering stitch along finished line, turn under seam allowance and press to form heart shape. Glue cardboard onto second piece.

5. Sandwich flannel between appliquéd and second pieces and overcast edges.

Couching
Pearl cotton, No.6 in blue

HOLY NIGHT

Pink

Star-shaped spangles

Straight st. with 3 strands of floss in salmon pink.

Yellow

Light blue

Blue

6. Place finished picture in rattan basket. Attach ribbon and tie knot.

Heart-shaped Ornament

Materials: Cotton fabric: Blue, 35cm by 20cm (14″×8″); scraps of pink, yellow, light blue and blue for appliqué. Striped ribbon, 1cm by 30cm (⅜″×12″). 10 pieces of small and one of large star-shaped spangles. Pearl cotton, No.5 in blue. Six-strand embroidery floss, No.25 in salmon pink and blue. Iron-on interfacing, flannel and cardboard, 20cm (8″) square each. Heart-shaped rattan basket (same size as pattern), 4cm (1 ⅝″) deep. Glue.
Finished size: See diagrams.

Knitters are the stars of Christmas,
and they'll all get awards for these superb designs—from the holiday pillows
to a very special holiday sweater.

Knitted Pillows
Instructions on page 40

Sweater
Instructions on page 43

Decorate with Teddy Bears

Teddy bears have a special holiday status—in little people's dreams and grown-up memories.
Indulge both with teddy motifs on gifts or giftwraps.

Teddy Bears
Instructions on page

Gift Bags
Instructions on page 57

Gift Bags
Instructions on page 53

Appliqué pattern (Actual size)

Do not add seam allowance to felt except where pieces are overlapped.

Gift Bags

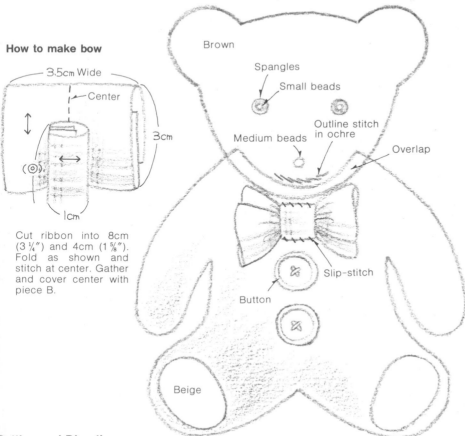

Brown

Spangles

Small beads

Medium beads

Outline stitch in ochre

Overlap

Slip-stitch

Button

Beige

How to make bow

3.5cm Wide

Center

3cm

1cm

Cut ribbon into 8cm (3 ¼") and 4cm (1 ⅝"). Fold as shown and stitch at center. Gather and cover center with piece B.

Materials: Checked cotton fabric: 46cm by 29cm (18 ⅜"×11 ⅝") for A and 38cm by 24cm (15 ¼"×9 ⅝") for B. Satin ribbon: Red, 0.5cm by 60cm for A; yellow, 0.5cm by 50cm for B. Felt for appliqué: Brown, 20cm by 10cm (8"×4") and scrap of beige. Checked ribbon, 3.5cm by 12cm (1 ⅜" × 4 ¾"). 2 buttons, 1.1cm (⅜") in diameter. One large, one medium and 2 small beads. 2 spangles. Six-strand embroidery floss, No.25 in ochre.

Finished size: A, 20cm by 24cm (8"×9 ⅝"). B, 16cm by 19cm (6 ⅜"×7 ⅝").

Cutting and Directions

Add seam allowance indicated in parentheses. Zigzag-stitch along raw edges.

A

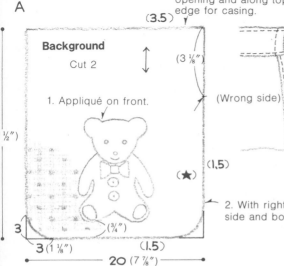

Background

Cut 2

1. Appliqué on front.

½"

(3.5)

(3 ⅛")

(Wrong side)

(★)

(1.5)

3

(¾")

3 (1 ⅛")

(1.5)

20 (7 ⅞")

2. With right sides facing, sew side and bottom seams.

4. Insert ribbon into casing. Thread bead and tie ends.

3. Stitch along side opening and along top edge for casing.

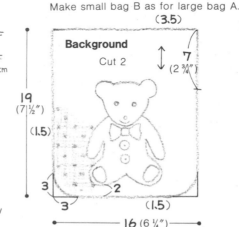

b

2cm

a

(Wrong side)

(★)

Make small bag B as for large bag A.

(3.5)

Background

Cut 2

7 (2 ¾")

19 (7 ½")

(1.5)

3

3

2

(1.5)

16 (6 ¼")

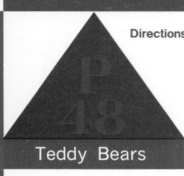

P 48

Teddy Bears

1. With right sides facing, sew two ear pieces together. Turn to right side.

2. Sew side and center pieces together matching marks. Make features.

3. Sew face and head together with right sides facing catching ends of ears. Turn to right side, stuff with fiberfill and slip-stitch opening closed.

4. Sew two pieces of front body together.

5. Sew front and back bodies together easing curved line. Stuff with fiberfill and slip-stitch opening closed.

6. Sew pieces for leg together. Stuff with fiberfill and slip-stitch opening closed. Make arms.

7. Sew head onto body securely.

8. Attach arms and legs onto body with 2 strands of heavy-duty thread.

Straight stitch with 3 strands of floss

9. Place ribbon around neck and tie into bow

Leg

Body

Insert needle from this point.

Pull thread and tie knot.

Materials: Cotton fabric: Checks, 40cm by 35cm (16″ × 14″) and scrap of brown for A; brown prints, 50cm by 40cm (20″×16″) and scrap of beige for B. Green grosgrain ribbon: 1cm by 40cm (³⁄₈″×16″) for A and 1.4cm by 45cm (½″×18″) for B. Six-strand embroidery floss, No. 25 in black. Polyester fiberfill.
Finished size: A: 21cm (8³⁄₈″) high. B: 27cm (10¾″) high.

A Patterns (Actual size)

Add 0.4cm for seam allowance
Use checked fabric and 3 strands of floss unless otherwise indicated.

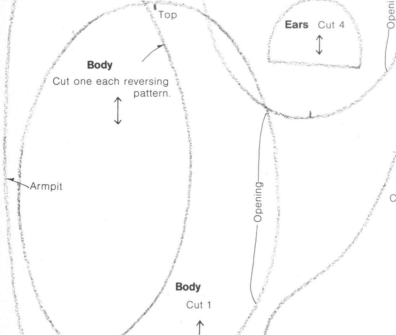

Top

Head Cut 1

Face (Front)
Cut 1

Opening

★

★

Satin st.

Attached ear

Face (side)
★ Cut one each
reversing pattern.

Satin st.

Ears Cut 4

Top

Body
Cut one each reversing pattern.

Armpit

Opening

Body
Cut 1

Attach leg onto body at X-marks

Arms
Cut two each reversing patterns.

Opening

Attach arm onto body at X-marks.

Legs
Cut two each reversing patterns.

Top

Opening

Sole
Brown Cut 2

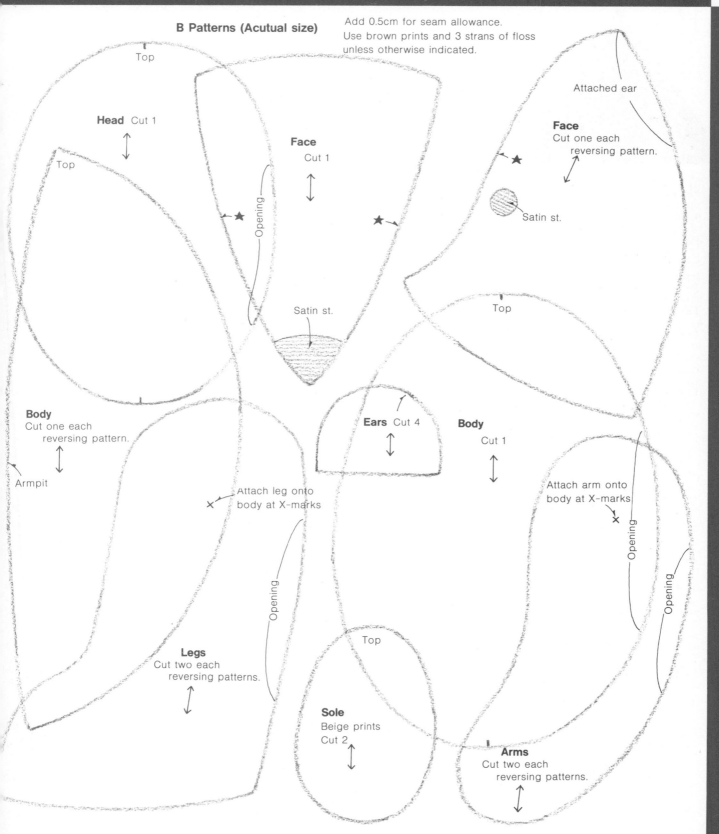

B Patterns (Acutual size)

Add 0.5cm for seam allowance.
Use brown prints and 3 strans of floss
unless otherwise indicated.

Top

Head Cut 1

Top

Attached ear

Face
Cut 1

Face
Cut one each
reversing pattern.

Opening

★

★

Satin st.

★

Satin st.

Top

Satin st.

Body
Cut one each
reversing pattern.

Armpit

Ears Cut 4

Body
Cut 1

Attach arm onto
body at X-marks

Opening

Attach leg onto
body at X-marks
✕

Opening

Opening

Top

Legs
Cut two each
reversing patterns.

Sole
Beige prints
Cut 2

Arms
Cut two each
reversing patterns.

P.50

Stuffed Ornaments

Patterns (Actual size) and Directions

Use various prints with Xmas designs. With right sides facing, sew two pieces together. Clip into curves and turn to right side. Stuff with fiberfill and slip-stitch opening closed.

Materials For one:

For Stocking: Print, 17cm by 11cm (6¾″ × 4⅜″). Satin ribbon, 0.6cm by 17cm (¼″ × 6¾″). Large and small beads, one each.

For Bear: Print, 19cm by 15cm (7⅝″ × 6″). Satin ribbon, 0.5cm by 17cm (¼″ × 6¾″). 4 pearl beads.

For Heart: Print, 14cm by 6cm (5⅝″ × 2⅜″). 10 pearl beads.

For Star: Print, 16cm by 8cm (6⅜″ × 3¼″). 5 pearl beads.

For Wreath: Print, 20cm by 10cm (8″ × 4″). Satin ribbon, 1.3 cm by 25cm (½″ × 10″). Braid, 0.5 cm by 45cm (¼″ × 18″). Polyester fiberfill.

Finished size: See patterns.

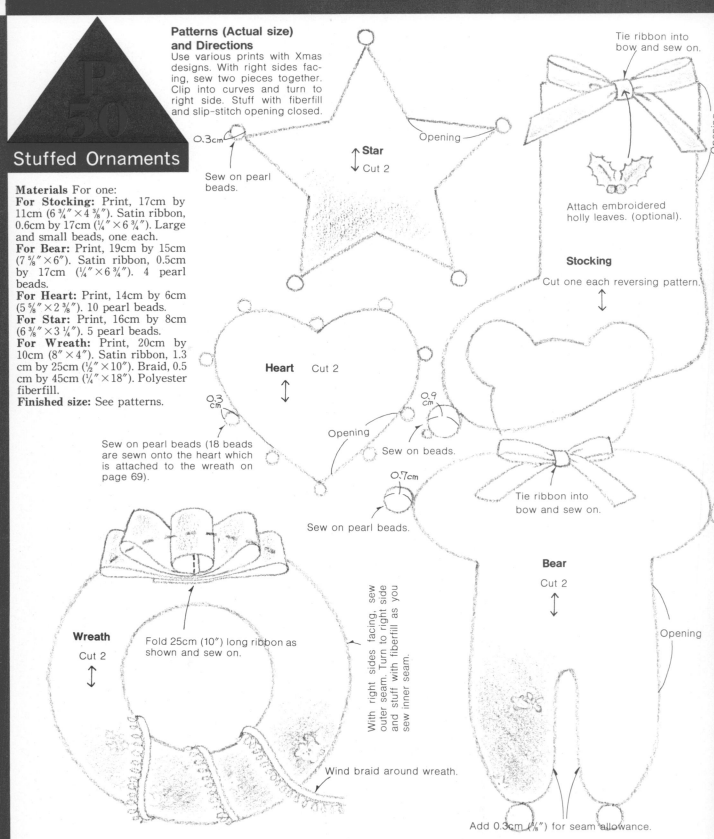

0.3cm

Sew on pearl beads.

↑ Star
↓ Cut 2

Opening

Tie ribbon into bow and sew on.

Attach embroidered holly leaves. (optional).

Stocking

Cut one each reversing pattern.

Heart Cut 2

0.3 cm

Opening

0.9 cm

Sew on beads.

Sew on pearl beads (18 beads are sewn onto the heart which is attached to the wreath on page 69).

0.7cm

Sew on pearl beads.

Tie ribbon into bow and sew on.

With right sides facing, sew outer seam. Turn to right side and stuff with fiberfill as you sew inner seam.

Bear
Cut 2

Opening

Wreath
Cut 2

Fold 25cm (10″) long ribbon as shown and sew on.

Wind braid around wreath.

Add 0.3cm (⅛″) for seam allowance.

Directions

Ready-made stick wreath with ornaments (see page 56), ribbon bow, leaves and bells.

How to make ribbon bow:

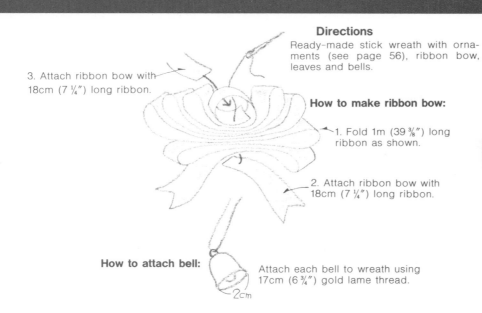

3. Attach ribbon bow with 18cm (7 ¼″) long ribbon.

1. Fold 1m (39 ⅜″) long ribbon as shown.

2. Attach ribbon bow with 18cm (7 ¼″) long ribbon.

How to attach bell:

Attach each bell to wreath using 17cm (6 ¾″) gold lame thread.

2cm

P 69
Wreath

Materials: Ornaments (see page 56). Ribbon with wire, 2.5cm by 125cm (1″×50″). Gold lamé thread. 5 gold leaves. 2 gold bells.
Finished size: 25cm (10″) in diameter.

★★★★★★★★★★★★★★★★★★★★★★★★★★★★★★★★★

P 51
Gift Bags

Materials: Cotton fabric: 42cm by 24cm (16 ¾″×9 ⅝″); 42cm by 12cm (16 ¾″×4 ¾″) for strip for casing. Scraps of felt for appliqué. Ribbon, 0.6cm by 15cm (¼″×6″). Cotton cord, 0.4cm by 50cm (⅛″×20″). Pearl cotton, No.5 in charcoal gray.
Finished size: 20cm by 27cm (8″×10 ¾″).

Cutting Diagrams

Add seam allowance indicated in parentheses.
Zigzag-stitch along raw edges.

No seam allowance

6
5
Fold
4.5
(1)
4.5
★

40

Fold

40

Directions

4. Make casing as shown below. (a) Stitch along side opening. (b) Fold strip in half lengthwise and top-stotch. (c) Top-stitch.

5. Insert cotton cord into casing and tiw ends.

2. With right sides facing, sew strip to bag. Turn to right side and top-stitch.
1. Appliqué.

6cm

3. With right sides facing, sew side and bottom seams.

1.7cm

a   c
★
Top-stitch
Wring side

Appliqué pattern (Actual size)

No seam allowance (Felt)
One strand of embroidery floss.

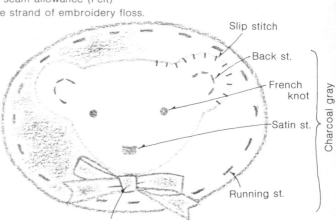

Slip stitch
Back st.
French knot
Satin st.
Running st.
Charcoal gray

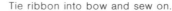

Tie ribbon into bow and sew on.

Pattern Appliqué Embroidery Designs (Actual size) and Directions

Cut appliqué pieces without adding seam allowance. Attach appliqué pieces onto background with glue, and then zigzag-stitch along edges.

5. Place flannel under background fabric. Overcast edges of front and back together catching fold of ribbon. Insert one end of ribbon through basket and tie into bow.

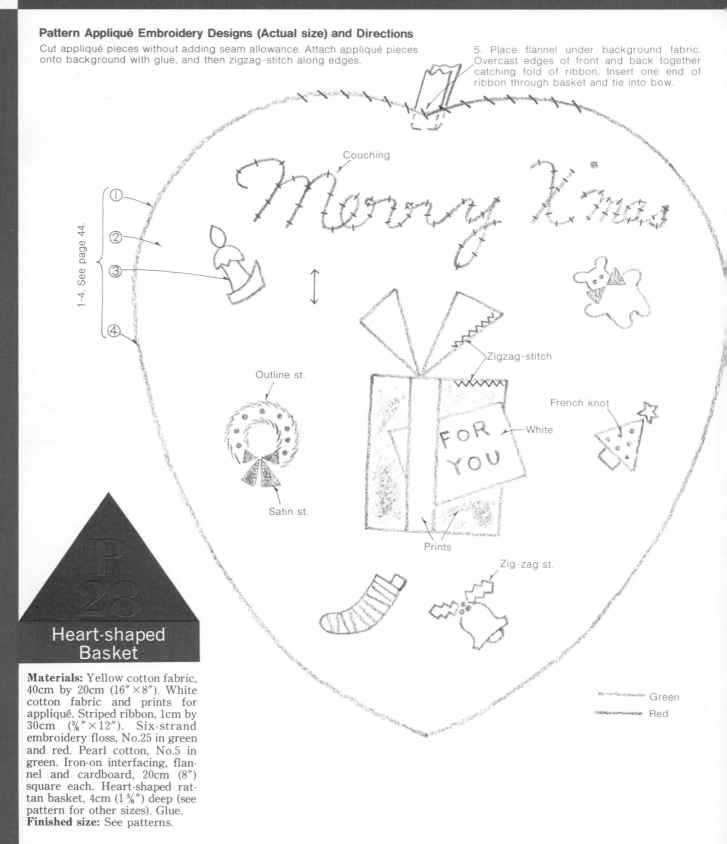

① ② ③ ④

1-4. See page 44.

Couching

Merry Xmas

Outline st.

Zigzag-stitch

French knot

White

FOR YOU

Satin st.

Prints

Zig-zag st.

Green
Red

P 28

Heart-shaped Basket

Materials: Yellow cotton fabric, 40cm by 20cm (16″×8″). White cotton fabric and prints for appliqué. Striped ribbon, 1cm by 30cm (³⁄₈″×12″). Six-strand embroidery floss, No.25 in green and red. Pearl cotton, No.5 in green. Iron-on interfacing, flannel and cardboard, 20cm (8″) square each. Heart-shaped rattan basket, 4cm (1 ⁵⁄₈″) deep (see pattern for other sizes). Glue.
Finished size: See patterns.

Gift Bag

Materials: Off-white wrinkled cotton fabric, 120cm by 43cm (48″×17 ¼″). White ribbon, 5cm by 105cm (2″×42″).
Finished size: 40cm by 60cm (16″×24″)

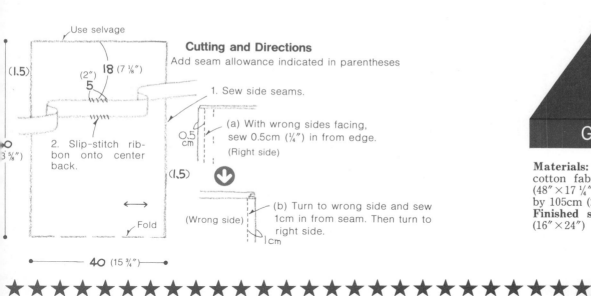

Use selvage

(1.5)

(2″) 18 (7 ⅛″)
5

(3 ⅝″)

2. Slip-stitch ribbon onto center back.

(1.5)

Fold

40 (15 ¾″)

Cutting and Directions
Add seam allowance indicated in parentheses

1. Sew side seams.

0.5 cm

(a) With wrong sides facing, sew 0.5cm (¼″) in from edge.
(Right side)

(Wrong side)

(b) Turn to wrong side and sew 1cm in from seam. Then turn to right side.

1cm

★★★★★★★★★★★★★★★★★★★★★★★★★★★★★★★★★★★★

Placemats and Coasters

Materials: For one: White organdy: 47cm by 34cm (18 ¾″× 13 ⅝″) for A; 16cm (6 ⅜″) square for B. White lace edging: 1cm by 160cm (⅜″×64″) for A; 1cm by 60cm (⅜″×24″) for B.
Finished size: A: 46.5cm by 33.5 cm (18 ⅝″ × 13 ⅜″) B: 15.5cm (6 ¼″) square.

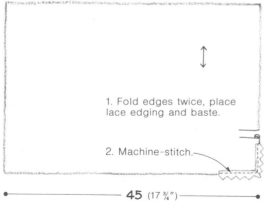

For Placemat:

32
(2 ⅝″)

1. Fold edges twice, place lace edging and baste.

2. Machine-stitch.

45 (17 ¾″)

Cutting and Directions
Add 1cm (⅜″) for seam allowance.

For Coaster:
Make as for Placemat.

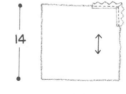

14

14 (5 ½″)

★★★★★★★★★★★★★★★★★★★★★★★★★★★★★★★★★★★★

Wall Hanging

Materials: White organdy, 83cm by 32cm (33 ¼″×12 ¾″). White lace edging (see photo), 1cm by 130cm (⅜″×52″). Several kinds of white ribbon, 19cm (7 ⅝″) long each.
Finished size: 32.5cm (13″) square

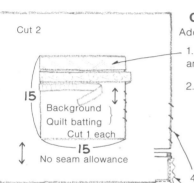

Cut 2

31

15

Background
Quilt batting
Cut 1 each

15

No seam allowance

31 (12 ¼″)

Cutting and Directions
Add seam allowance indicated in parentheses.

1. Place several kinds of ribbon on center square and slip-stitch.

2. Place appliquéd square on quilt batting and baste.

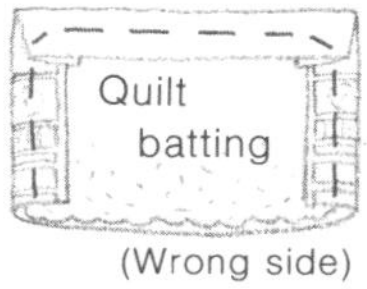

Quilt batting

(Wrong side)

3. Place padded square on background and slip-stitch.

4. Turn in seam allowance and overcast edges.

5. Sew on lace edging.

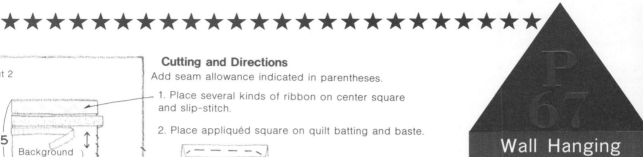

White Ornaments

Materials: For one: White flannel, 26cm by 13cm (10 ⅜″ × 5 ¼″). White satin ribbon, 0.4cm by 35cm (⅛″ × 14″). Polyester fiberfill.
Finished size: See patterns.

Directions

1. Sew 2 pieces together with right sides facing leaving opening for turning.
2. Clip into curves and turn to right side. Stuff with fiberfill and slip-stitch opening closed.
3. Sew on ribbon for hanging.

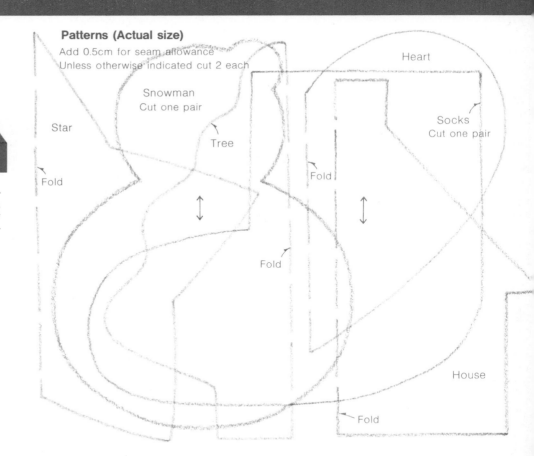

Patterns (Actual size)
Add 0.5cm for seam allowance
Unless otherwise indicated cut 2 each

Star
Fold

Snowman
Cut one pair

Tree
Fold

Heart

Socks
Cut one pair
Fold

Fold

House
Fold

Christmas Tree

Materials: Gold and silver laminated fabric, 65cm by 35cm (26″ × 14″) each. Pink and blue satin ribbon, 1.5cm by 72cm (⅝″ × 28 ¾″) each. Pearl beads: 300 round; 100 almond-shaped. Round beads: 12 large and 3 medium. 7 bamboo beads. One star-shaped bead. Spangles: 30 star shapes (large, medium and small); 3 moon shapes; one round. 6 rhine stones. Empty can, 5.5cm (2 ¼″) in diameter and 5.5cm (2 ¼″) deep. Polyester fiberfill. Glue.
Finished size: 35cm (14″) high.

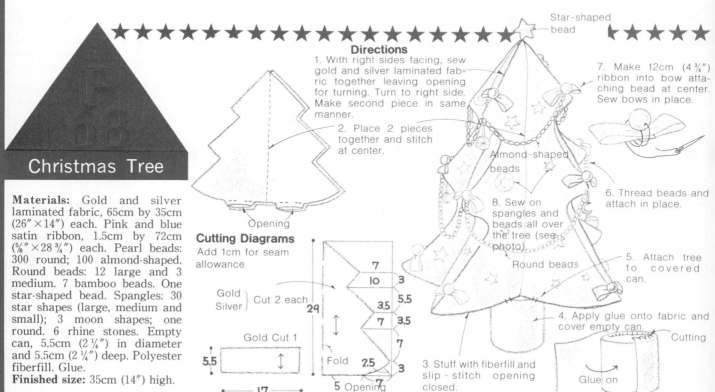

Directions

1. With right sides facing, sew gold and silver laminated fabric together leaving opening for turning. Turn to right side. Make second piece in same manner.
2. Place 2 pieces together and stitch at center.

Opening

Cutting Diagrams
Add 1cm for seam allowance

Gold } Cut 2 each
Silver }

Gold Cut 1

5.5

17

29

Fold

7
10   3
5.5
3.5
7   3.5
7
2.5   3
7
5 Opening
15

Star-shaped bead

7. Make 12cm (4 ¾″) ribbon into bow attaching bead at center. Sew bows in place.

Almond-shaped beads

6. Thread beads and attach in place.

8. Sew on spangles and beads all over the tree (see photo).

Round beads

5. Attach tree to covered can.

4. Apply glue onto fabric and cover empty can.

Cutting

Glue on

3. Stuff with fiberfill and slip-stitch opening closed.

Cutting Diagrams and Directions

Add seam allowance indicated in parentheses.

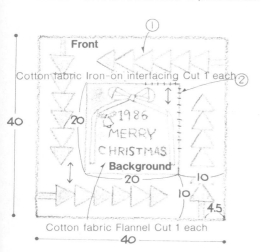

Front

Cotton fabric Iron-on interfacing Cut 1 each

40 20 10 10 4.5

1986 MERRY CHRISTMAS

Background

20 10

Cotton fabric Flannel Cut 1 each

40

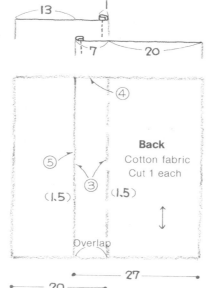

13 7 20

Back
Cotton fabric
Cut 1 each

(1.5) (1.5)

Overlap

20 27

1. Press iron-on interfacing on wrong side of front. Appliqué trees in zigzag-stitch.

2. Embroider letters and bell on center fabric.

3. Fold edges of back piece twice and stitch.

4. Overlap 7cm (2¾″) each of back pieces. With right sides facing, sew front and back pieces together. Turn to right side.

5. Insert inner pillow.

Embroidery Patterns

See page 10.

Bullion knot with 1 strand of floss No.5 in red.

Zigzag stitch with 3 strands of floss No. 25 in green.

Tie ribbon to bow and slip-stitch.

1986

Couching with 1 strand of floss No.25 in red.

MERRY

CHRISTMAS

2cm

Christmas Pillows

Materials: For A: Cotton fabric: Pink,94cm by 42cm (37 ⅝″× 16 ¾″); cobalt blue, 22cm (8 ¾″) square; scraps of green prints for appliqué. Ribbon, 1cm by 70cm (⅜″×28″). Pearl cotton, No.5 in red. Six-strand embroidery floss, No.25 in green and red. Iron-on interfacing, 60cm by 40cm (24″×16″). Flannel, 20cm (8″) square. Inner pillow stuffed with kapok 40cm (16″) square. For B: Cotton fabric: Blue, 94cm by 42cm (37 ⅝″×16 ¾″); blue and white stripes, 22cm (8 ¾″) square. Scraps of green prints. Ribbon, 1cm by 70cm (⅜″×28″). Pearl cotton, No.5 in navy and red. Six-strand embroidery floss, No.25 in green and navy. Iron-on interfacing, 60cm by 40cm (24″× 16″). Flannel, 20cm (8″) square. Inner pillow stuffed with kapok, 40cm (16″) square.
Finished size: 40cm (16″) square.

Appliqué Patterns (Actual size)

Press iron-on interfacing on wrong side og appliqué pieces and cut them without adding seam allowance.

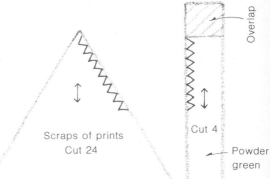

Scraps of prints
Cut 24

Cut 4

Overlap

Powder green

Gift Box

Materials: Cotton fabric. Ribbon. Quilt batting.
Finished size: Small box: 11cm (4 ⅜") wide. Large box: 16cm (6 ⅜") wide.

Cutting Diagrams and Directions

Use ready-made boxes.
1. Cut fabric to the size of lid adding 1.5cm (⅝") for seam allowance.

2. Cut batting same size as lid.

3. Run a gathering stitch along side of lid.

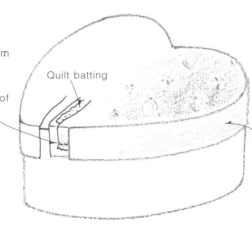

Quilt batting

4. Glue ribbon side of lid.

★★★★★★★★★★★★★★★★★★★★★★★★★★★★★★★★★★★★

Christmas Tree Picture

Materials: For one: White cotton fabric with gold dots, 15cm by 20cm (6"×8"). Various kinds of ribbon and one round bead. 15 – 18 bamboo beads. 2 large and one small star-shaped spangles. Flannel and cardboard, 11cm by 15cm each. Glue. Frame, 9.5cm by 14cm (3 ¾"×5 ⅝")(inside measurement).
Finished size: Same size as frame.

Directions

1. Appliqué assorted ribbons and mogol on background fabric in slip-stitch to form Xmas tree.
2. Place appliqué fabric and sew on spangles and beads.
3. Place decorated fabric on cardboard and glue. Frame.

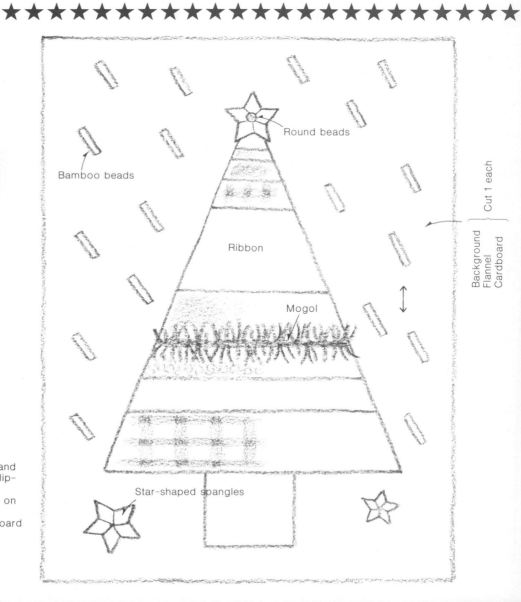

Round beads

Bamboo beads

Ribbon

Mogol

Background Flannel Cardboard
Cut 1 each

Star-shaped spangles

Directions

Make ribbon (see page and sew on.

5.5cm · 2.5cm

0.9cm · 5cm

5. Fold 15cm (6") ribbon in half and sew in place.

3.5cm

4. Turn to right side. Turn under seam allowance and slip-stitch.

1. With right sides facing, sew 2 pieces together leaving top edge open.

2. Sew ends of green band with right sides facing.

14cm

0.7cm

3. Sew green band to top edge with right sides facing.

(Wrong side)

No seam allowance

Patterns (Actual size)

Add seam allowance indicated in parentheses
Zigzag-stitch along raw edges.

(1.5)

Top edge open.
Cut 1

Fold

(1)

(1)

Materials: Quilted fabric with design, 32cm by 18cm (12 ¾" × 7 ¼"). Powder green satin ribbon, 18cm by 6cm (7 ¼" × 2 ⅜"). Ribbon: 0.9cm by 15cm (⅜" × 6"); 2.5cm by 20cm (1" × 8").
Finished size: See diagrams.

How to cut fabric

Place open-heart-shaped Styrofoam on fabric and draw outline. Cut fabris adding same measurement of thickness of Styrofoam and 1cm (⅜") for seam allowance.

P 71

Stuffed Open Heart

How to make bow

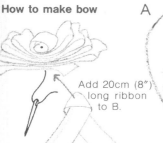

Add 20cm (8") long ribbon to B.

A

2cm

5. Attach bell and holly leaf

Directions

1. With right sides facing, sew inner edges together. Clip into seem.

2. Cover Styrofoam with fabric matshing inner edge. Turn outer edges in and slip-stitch. Clip into seam if necessary to prevent wrinkles.

3. Fold 70cm (28") long ribbon into bow and sew on.

4. Wind 160cm (64") long ribbon and beaded tape around heart.

Materials: Prints with X mas design: 60cm by 30cm (24" × 12") for A and 40cm by 20cm (16" × 8") for B. 2.5cm (1") wide ribbon with wire: Graded pink, .230cm (92") for A and graded blue, 90cm (36") for B. White beaded tape, 160cm (64"). Artificial holly leaf. Gold bell. Open-shaped Styrofoam: 25cm by 24cm (10" × 9 ⅝") for A and 16cm by 15cm (6 ⅜" × 6") for B.
Finished size: Same size as Styrofoam.

Boxed Ornaments

How to make center square

(a) Embroider and decorate with beads or spangles as indicated on white fabric.

(b) Place cardboard on wrong side of fabric, place two-sided adhesive tape alomg edge and turn margin over cardboard.

(c) Attach finished square in place.

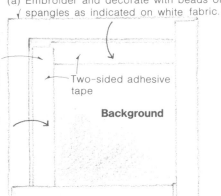

Two-sided adhesive tape

Background

Embroidery Patterns (Actual size)

Cut center square from white fabric adding 1cm for seam allowance. Work running stitch with 6 strands of red floss.

White

Running stitch with 6 strands of floss in red.

MERRY CHRISTMAS

2 strands of floss in red.

Sew star-shaped spangle with bead.

Running stitch with 2 strands of floss in red.

3 strands of floss in green.

Attach two ribbon bows.

Sew on bell

0.8cm

3 strands of folss in red.

3 strands of floss in green.

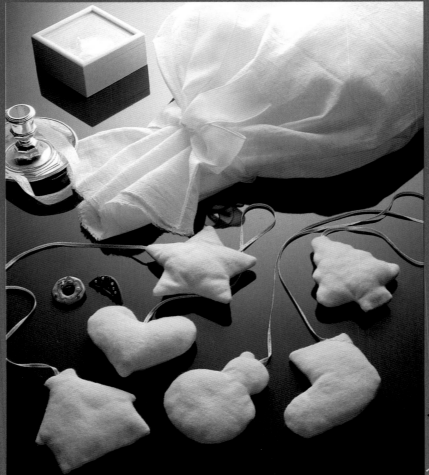

White Ornaments
Instructions on pages 59 & 60

*The exquisite look of winter white wins everyone's attention,
whether in a few classic decorations or splendidly simple linens.
The tone is deft, understated—and elegant.*

White Placemats and Coasters
Instructions on page 59

White Wall Hanging
Instructions on page 59

Stuffed Christmas Tree
Instructions on page 60

Happy Christmas

*Here are memories for many a Christmas, when you begin this year
to make these wonderful designs for your home or for gifts.*

Wreath
Instructions on page 57

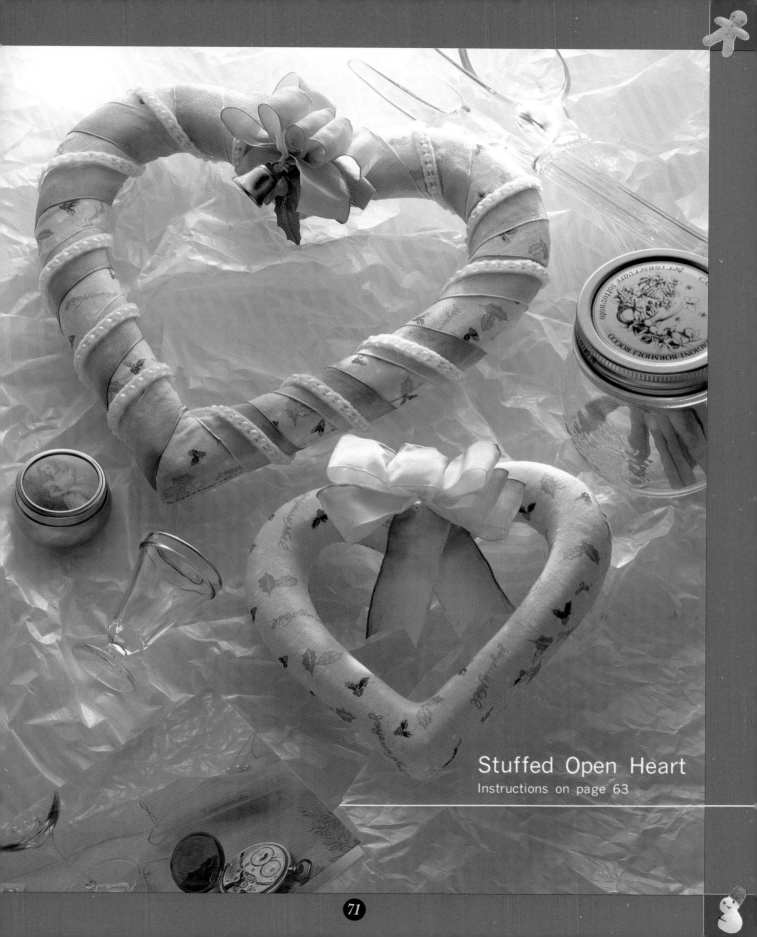

Stuffed Open Heart

Instructions on page 63

Christmas Pillows
Instructions on page 61